# THE
# SKYJACKER

# T H E
# SKYJACKER
## His Flights of Fantasy

*DAVID G. HUBBARD, M.D.*

*The Macmillan Company, New York, New York*
*Collier-Macmillan Ltd., London*

The Macmillan Company
866 Third Avenue, New York, N.Y. 10022
Collier-Macmillan Canada Ltd., Toronto, Ontario

Library of Congress Catalog Card Number: 76-127940

First Printing

Printed in the United States of America

Permission to reprint the two lines of poetry on p. 37 by W. H. Auden is gratefully acknowledged. Copyright © 1966 by W. H. Auden. Untitled poem on p. 43 of "Shorts," *Collected Shorter Poems 1927–1957*, published by Random House, Inc.

*To my wife, Bettie*

# CONTENTS

# Introduction

The objective of this book is to introduce the criterion of common sense to the subject of skyjacking [1] for the simple reason that the only criterion applied to it for nearly a decade—by the public, by government agencies, by news media—has been that of hysteria.

The problems of skyjacking were obviously capable of evoking hysteria on many fronts, but not of spurring the federal government into a study of these problems. It became clear to me quite some time ago that the study of offenders was the only approach to the solution of these problems, and this book is based on such study, carried out over a period of almost two years. It is intended as criticism. Its purpose is to serve as a catalyst, to break the barriers between the various departments and institutions concerned with skyjacking, and to offer at least one avenue of understanding.

Originally, I conceived the study in the form of an article in a medical journal, limited to the case histories of twelve skyjackers. It soon became clear, however, that the subject demanded wider exploration, and I finally decided in favor of a book-length study aimed at the general public.

It must be made clear that the conclusions I have drawn are speculative and intuitive, even if they represent the speculation and intuition of one with many years of psychiatric practice. Also, in some instances the book reflects the virtual absence of other re-

---

[1] This usage is not an affectation, as will appear later in Chapter XVI.

search in the area, together with the fact that clinical material is closely guarded in federal facilities, which forecloses the possibility of pursuing inquiry toward more conclusive findings.

Much must be done to prove or disprove the theories set forth here, and in particular, I hope to stimulate the type of research that might bridge the abyss of unreality between the problem and the methods of solution. Also, I should like to emphasize that the current medical, psychiatric, and psychological literature fails to touch upon the subject of the physical force of gravity and motion in regard to its potential importance in the psychology of man. Here, too, my theoretical formulations are offered in the dual role of personal speculation and stimulus for inquiries by others.

I was enabled to undertake this study by a grant from an individual who has made one stipulation and one assumption. His stipulation was anonymity for himself. His assumption was that, even if the theories presented here should prove to be unsubstantiated, they might nevertheless demonstrate wide enough gaps in existing knowledge to oblige more able men to enter the field in order to narrow them.

Special gratitude is felt toward those federal career medical officers, who made this material available and guided me through the bureaucratic maze, at Washington, long after the study had become anathema to non-medical bureaucrats.

My secretaries, Joyce Saur, Gloria Gannaway, and Sarah Peeples, worked under circumstances that were often less than ideal, as well as against most unreasonable deadlines. Kay Owens and Kathy Robertson dug out research data with relentless probity, while W. J. A. Power, Ph.D., wielded the editorial blue pencil with unfailing accuracy. Martha Heimberg edited speaking papers into acceptability.

My deepest gratitude goes to the imprisoned skyjackers themselves. At the end of every interview, each one expressed the hope that he had been helpful. Each one was.

# Prologue

In August, 1968, it was hot in Key West. The sun was bright and the city was clean and astir with all the activities of an early workday morning. Beyond it lay the Caribbean. This, the southernmost tip of the United States, has often been described as land's end, which to certain depressed people means that it is the jumping-off place, the place beyond which there is nothing more. One day that month, in a small park, near a high-rise hotel, a single figure seated on a park bench was slumped and curled in the dejected posture men have adopted throughout the ages as a reflection of their grief. He gently rocked back and forth. His name was Brian.

For months he had been aware of the fact that he, the "Rock of Gibraltar" of his family, was crumbling. He could no longer be the strength of his family, to aid and support those about him with financial assistance or personal advice, because some terrible thing was going on inside him. He was beset by fears, doubts, and concerns of such an order that he had come to despise himself and pray for death. During the months prior to his arrival in Key West, he had flown from his home in the Northeast to Miami seven or eight times and, on one occasion, had even gone as far as Mexico with the intention of disappearing there. He wanted to escape the failure of his personal existence. Each of his attempts to run away or disappear had failed when it had become evident that he was unable to support himself because of the intensity of the emotional reaction he was undergoing.

On this, his last trip to Miami, his resolve to go and never to return was stronger than ever before, stronger even than the time he had gone to Mexico City. He had taken with him that time all of his small supplies, even including, as he said, "his tennis shoes." While in Mexico, he had made application to the Cuban Consulate for a visa to Cuba. It was denied and he had returned to the Northeast. Now on this his last trip to Miami, he was strongly resolved to complete some action.

After a day or two in Miami, where his discomfort was most acute, he had felt himself to be still too close to the things that he believed to be the sources of his anxiety and troubles. He purchased a bus ticket to Key West. He was certain he was being followed and assumed that it was by the FBI. When he had arrived there the evening before, he had checked into a high-rise hotel and was placed on the twentieth floor. He could not abide the room. The opportunities for success in a suicidal effort were too great. It would be *so* easy to jump out that window and fall, not just the twenty floors to the earth, but to plunge right on down into Hell.

He was a Catholic and, he believed, a good one. But he wanted to commit suicide. Under the rules of Catholicism, as he understood them, a man who destroys his own life is irretrievably condemned to Hell and foregoes, for all time, the opportunity of joining his Maker.

The evening before, when he checked into the hotel, he carried with him a small paper bag full of aspirin and other medicines which, he told the bellboy, he would sell in Cuba for several thousand dollars.

Shortly after checking in, he called a boat rental company and inquired as to the possibility of renting a boat, saying that the following day he would like to sail out into the Gulf in order to meet his sister who would "be passing by that way on a large yacht in which she and several of her friends were traveling." The impression he hoped to make was that of a wealthy bon vivant. When his telephone call began to turn a little sour, because of the suspicions of the owner of the boat company to whom the conversation did not seem quite consistent, he terminated the call and left the room as promptly as possible.

Down in the area of the harbor, he found a small boat owner who was willing to rent him a small sailboat for cruising about. Since he wanted to be well out into the Gulf by afternoon, he quickly cast off, set sail, and moved some short distance from the land, at which point he lashed the tiller with the boat headed toward mid-Caribbean. In his fantasy, the winds would freshen and ultimately tip the small boat over, causing him to drown. It was his intention to die by the force of the elements so that his death would not be his personal responsibility. He lay down in the bottom of the boat and began to recite to himself various parts of Scripture and fragments of the liturgy of the church.

He felt the surge of the water about him and could hear the lapping of the waves upon the hull of the boat. The skies above were blue and marked only by an occasional soft, floating white cloud. He was filled with a great sense of ecstasy and with a deep and abiding contentment, floating, suspended as it were, between the earth and the heavens, awaiting that glorious moment when God would clasp him to his bosom. Suddenly, there was a harsh grating sound from the bow of the boat. He clambered up and found that the boat had beached itself on a small bit of sand, not more than a hundred yards from the spot where he had rented it. So he returned the boat to its owner, inwardly shamefaced and apologetic. Now, his last few dollars had been spent on the hire of the boat, and he was again totally dependent upon his family, for he had called home earlier in the day asking for money to be sent by wire so that he could return.

Returning home by wiring for funds had occurred time and again, and he felt terribly ashamed at his inability to get away. The thought of facing his family and others who would be aware of his illness was quite intolerable. The thought of a woman's laughing at him seemed particularly cruel. He spent the night in the park, rocking gently to and fro in an attempt to find some workable solution through which he could die without the guilt of his death being upon his own hands. By morning, he had an answer.

It would all be really quite simple. He would get his money from Western Union, buy a pistol, go to a bank, and attempt to hold it up. In the course of this action, a guard would see him and attempt to stop him. In the process, he would be shot and would die and thereby achieve his purpose. Accordingly, when dawn came, he got some breakfast and went to a nearby used gun shop from which he purchased a small revolver. When the revolver lay in his hand, cold, hard, metallic, the thought flashed through his mind that, although this action was logically well conceived, there was an ethical objection to it, for he would be putting himself upon the conscience of the guard who was to kill him. Somehow, this did not seem quite right to him, so the plan was abandoned.

After reading the morning papers and *Time* magazine, where he read about the continuing rash of skyjackings, he decided to return to an older plan, under which he had once applied for a visa to Cuba but had been refused. He had thought that if he could get to Cuba he could solve his problem. Since he was such a good Catholic, he would be offensive to Fidel Castro, who, in turn, would order his death. He literally believed that Castro was the Devil. It seemed quite fitting, somehow, to make his death the act of the Devil, who would thereby free him to go to God. Since it was not possible for him to enter Cuba legally by a visa for this purpose, he would skyjack an airplane.

While walking to the airline office to obtain his ticket, however, he was again assailed by his religious scruples with the thought that, in the attempt to achieve his own death, he would endanger the lives of perhaps as many as a hundred other individuals who would be in the plane. This was really unacceptable to him. In addition, he was not quite sure that he had enough money to buy a ticket on a commercial airliner. Then the thought struck him that he might well charter a small aircraft, because one paid for a charter at the end of the flight. He learned this some months before when he chartered an aircraft to travel between two North-eastern cities. He went to Key West Airport, entered a local aircraft charter service, and engaged the services of a young and amiable pilot who was, ostensibly, to fly him from Key West to Miami in a Cessna 210.

When the plane took off, he felt that same exultant ecstasy he always experienced when a plane suddenly rose. When the flight was one which was to take him farther away from those who troubled and bedeviled him, he was especially euphoric. On the other hand, he could remember the countless times that he had returned home in defeat from his various attempts at running away, and inevitably, as the plane approached his home airport, he would become tense, and his unbearable headaches would return. When the plane sank toward the runway, he would experience indescribable despair.

After they had flown for only a few minutes, he quietly uncovered his pistol and instructed the pilot to fly to Cuba. He was, in this moment, coldly, coolly, and calmly determined to use the weapon he carried in order to achieve his purpose. In that instant, there was little doubt in his mind that he would use it if need be.

When the city of Havana came into view, he felt an increasing excitement, and as the plane touched down on the runway at Jose Marti Airport, he experienced a great sense of successful completion of his goal.

At the moment when he revealed his gun and his objective, he became a *skyjacker*.

# I

# Skyjackers: The Beginning

## SKYJACKING IN GENERAL

At the time this man acted, national concern had been increasingly alerted to a new and frightening phenomenon. Sinister individuals had made it their business to capture aircraft and to direct their courses to an alien and unfriendly land from which the culprits seemed never to emerge. Ordinary citizens (and officialdom) had been left bewildered by the antics of the skyjackers, uncertain of their motives, and at a loss to explain why anyone should elect such a bizarre way to leave a land whose gates, it was assumed, were open for all who wish to depart. As a nation, we found ourselves humiliated. We were able neither to retaliate against these offenders nor to control them. Like an elephant with a gallstone, we were thrashing about in great pain and in fear of the unknown. Meanwhile, the affliction steadily worsened. We held our breaths in dread anticipation of the catastrophe that must surely occur, as much overcome by the threat of personal loss as by the international complications that would follow such an event. But our national attitude toward the crime had not been totally negative. Indeed, it seemed at times to be a mixture of outrage and delight, not unlike that of the parent who finds himself helpless to control the behavior of a child engaged in acting out some fantasy which we vicariously enjoy. The result was that airline passengers sometimes foolishly joked with a stewardess when boarding a plane by inquiring, "Havana?" Such a remark sometimes entitled the joker to a good laugh at the county jail.

Undoubtedly, there had been many different types of people involved in these crimes, and undoubtedly their reasons varied, but their actions had given support to those in this world who were unfriendly to this nation. They had made it appear to be a gigantic prison from which one escaped, gun in hand, aboard a stolen airplane. The popular fancy at home, aided and abetted by the news media, had evolved a number of hypotheses to explain the situation: Perhaps some of the skyjackers had been Cuban agents bent on our humiliation. (Though the Cuban government seemed to be as bewildered and uncomfortable about the incidents as we were. Neither government, however, had been able to devise a formula that would accommodate our mutual differences in such a manner as to bring these offenses to a halt.) It was considered probable that some of the offenders had been grief-stricken Cuban immigrants to this country, no longer able to tolerate separation from their loved ones, who had tried this desperate maneuver in order to return to their families. Of course, it is natural enough that when there has been an abrupt change in the political control of a nation, a certain number of people will flee across its borders only to become aware later of their homesickness and their need of family and friends, and who must then go home, whether home belongs to Castro or to the Devil himself. Again, it could have been that some were agents of other powers who had taken this opportunity to create security gaps through which to move our nation's secrets. Or, better still, perhaps they had all been criminals fleeing from the law. Or, of course, they were political deviates!

To me, it seems far more likely that there are two more reasonable root causes. The first is that individuals who are seriously sick in a psychiatric sense are using this action either as a direct expression of their illness or as acted-out behavior to escape some less personally acceptable intent. The causes of their defection, therefore, may be as variable as the causes of their illness. And, second, it appears to me, on the basis of my research into this matter, that a mood of national hysteria is involved, which sets loose a mob dynamic into which susceptible individuals are drawn. In many instances, both of these factors are involved; that is to say, certain sick people are swept up by the current mob psychology to perform this act which, in its own way, is a direct, symbolic dramatization of their own lunacy, as well as that of the community about them. Most Americans observed this strange phenomenon with a mixture of curiosity and resentment. Because of professional training, there were various specific things that aroused my curiosity. The attitude of the press, however, based upon its own investigation and upon those of the regular law agencies, conditioned most of my thinking. From time to time, like many men interested in mechanics, I had idly speculated on various capturing devices that would trap, stab, gas, electrocute, or throw the culprit through a trap door in the floor of the craft. Basically, however, it did not really matter to me and it seemed likely that the federal government would handle it. During my idle speculation, in the summer of 1968, it seemed unlikely that these unusual men would shortly become a major preoccupation of mine.

For the average American, the year 1968 had been one of unrest. The war in Vietnam had gone badly and had been escalated several times with no significant improvement in our affairs. The first large contingent of disgruntled servicemen had been released. Their voices could be heard in the land.

In February of that election year, President Lyndon Johnson announced that he would not run for re-election, thereby throwing the Democratic party open to an active process of candidate selection. The Republicans were equally engaged in an attempt to find a candidate for President, although the outcome seemed reasonably certain. By this time, cities had been burned and universities had been sacked. The use of hallucinogenic drugs and "draft dodging" were common expressions of unrest.

By that August, skyjacking had become a rather common practice, with the theft of one chartered airplane, four large American transports, and three large South American transports—all of which had flown to Cuba.

In August, two men skyjacked aircraft twelve hundred miles apart—the first (the man in the Prologue) from Key West, Florida, and the second from the environs of Washington, D.C. Their attempts were separated by only a few hours, and their common destination was Cuba, albeit for very different reasons.

Between that day, in August of 1968, and the end of the year, both men spent most of their time in jails, one in Cuba and the other in Miami.

On the national scene, Humphrey and Nixon won the nominations of their respective parties. Nixon won the election. By crowding the NASA time schedule, man orbited the moon during the administration of President Johnson.

Skyjacking proceeded at an unprecedented pace. So did the rise in the stock market and the cost of living.

January 1, 1969 found both men federal prisoners awaiting medical evaluation prior to trial.


## MY FIRST SKYJACKERS

Six months after the crimes, it came about that I met them both at a federal prison facility where I served as consultant. It is the psychiatric court of final appeal for the entire federal bench, as well as the federal prison system. As such, I had felt sure it would offer interesting variations from my more pedestrian civilian practice. On that day, I was to begin an unforeseen and unplanned two-year research project of skyjackers.

The facility was a great distance from Dallas, where I live and maintain my private practice, and it was mutually agreed that I would spend a full day there each month. In the course of the day, two or three patients would be interviewed. Such an arrangement was fatiguing, but the pressure tended to enhance the sensitivity of the staff, much as certain marathon group experiences are said to do.

Prior to my departure from Dallas, Dr. Wayne Glotfelty, director of the Department of Psychiatry at the facility, called to inform me that we would be asked to see several men, who had recently committed identical crimes thousands of miles apart. Violation of our national boundaries was involved. I assumed that they would be "draft dodgers," like those who had recently been flowing out through our borders. A number of these had returned and had been interviewed before the group in preceding months.

In connection with these draft evaders, we opened the meeting with discussion of the patients seen the previous month. It was proposed that we establish "Export Centers" for those individuals whose lives had become so fouled up that it was now impossible for them to stay here and to face up to that loathesome reality. The observation was made that this nation had long flattered itself with the thought that its arms were always open to receive "the huddled masses" who flee to us from various tyrannies, but that perhaps we had now come to a time when we no longer had a "western frontier" into which our own maladjusted could retreat to die or to begin life again. It seemed likely that we had our own "huddled masses," but that we were much too vain to face the fact.

Contrary to my expectation, however, Dr. Glotfelty informed us that he intended to present, for diagnosis and discussion two skyjackers.

On this particular day—in early January, 1969—the project began. The first skyjacker to enter the room was Brian (of the Prologue). He seemed meek and mild—not the sort of person one would assume capable of violent acts. His voice was very soft and gentle. It quickly became evident that he had been following an intensely religious way of life for a long time. This system was inadequate, and he failed miserably. He became psychotic and planned his own death. But, even in psychosis, he could not commit suicide because he felt that the act would have condemned him to Hell.

So he committed a statutory crime for which the penalty was death. In a sense, therefore, he committed a secular crime to escape sin and its consequences. He had, as far as he was concerned, remained true to God and to his religious scruples, no matter what his secular crimes might have been. The story that he told in the interview was consistent, internally coherent, and natural throughout. One could not question its validity, and there was no evidence that he was being calculating or that he was guilty of malingering.

I might note that he once planned to be a monk and spent four years in a monastery. He wanted to enter the most contemplative and disciplined order of his church.

The second skyjacker, Elmer, appeared to have developed along much the same lines. He had also failed in life, but, instead of developing suicidal wishes, he moved steadily toward murder. (Psychiatrists consider suicidal and murderous wishes to be, in general, affectively identical, the only difference being that the former is directed against the self and the latter against another person.) Elmer was brought up in the Church of God.

Although he channeled his violent anti-social drives toward murder, his religious prohibition against violence forced the drives into a single symbolic act. This act was not, ultimately, inconsistent with his understanding of God's demands, even though it was a statutory crime. He, like Brian, chose an earthly executioner.

The conference discussion following these cases was sprightly. In some strange way, in spite of the fatigue of eight straight hours of interview, we were all stimulated at the thought of these strange, gentle, religious men individually challenging the secular powers about them. Somehow, they seemed related, particularly in the sense of their perception of "another world" in which they already partially lived. It was apparent that their worldly actions were precisely designed to facilitate their direct ascension to God, even though those actions might upset "the rulers of this world." They were somehow free of burdens, although, figuratively speaking, they were in chains, and, literally, they were behind bars. Their speech was soft and light. They appeared untouched by the daily realities of the prison life about them.

The discussion moved to a recognition of their deep sense of masculine failure and to the threat of emergent homosexuality. We then noted their successive regressions to paranoid schizophrenic reactions which were accompanied by inpourings of crude, murderous/suicidal introjected paternal impulses. This was followed by the ultimate acted-out behavior, the skyjacking, which was designed to release their tremendous destructive drives and, simultaneously, to render them harmless through the symbolic quality of the act. As a consequence of this act, they were charged with a statutory crime, rather than found guilty of mortal sin.

Based on our notes, their cases were put in the form of sketchy case histories, less detailed and simpler than those of the skyjackers who were to be tracked down subsequently.

## THE CASE OF BRIAN

Brian came near to becoming a Catholic priest. He was now thirty-three and his aims, both personal and professional, had been defeated. He was the only male child, with three younger female siblings—one of them retarded. The father was an alcoholic with such a level of violence and hostility "that all the kids grew up and got out as fast as they could." The mother was a very strict and devout Catholic who tried to offer the children her strong Christian image to offset the sinful image constructed by the father. She won them all from the father through many infantile years of struggle. So much so, that Brian came to understand only partially, if at all, the role of the male in society. His only image of that function was that of a celibate priest, which his mother very strongly urged him to be. "She and the Sisters told me I had a vocation to be a priest, but, of course, that was to be after I had taken care of my sisters' troubles by helping them get married." His father stopped drinking when the patient was twelve years of age, but no valuable relationship ever developed. Brian felt that his father favored the girls.

As a child, he often dreamed that "something was after me, my body was heavy, heavy, heavy." He recalled night as being difficult, because "it always seemed something awful was about to happen." He had poor muscular coordination, wasn't good in sports, and was rarely chosen for them.

Accordingly, he was studious, slow, and introverted throughout high school. He had one mildly erotic attachment to a girl, which slowly grew during their joint school study effort. After this episode, he said of dating, "I didn't date because I didn't know how to ask."

After graduating, "I worked in different department stores for four years in an attempt to earn money to make it possible for the girls to get good husbands." During this time, there was one important involvement, emotional only, with a widow with two children. He was humiliated by the taunts of his sisters for his choice of a girlfriend and immediately dropped her. He entered a monastery after the last of his sisters was married off and completed almost all of the first four years. He described this time as "the best years of my life. I didn't have to think for myself." When the husband of one of his sisters died suddenly, and the sister herself became psychotic, he resigned from his studies and went for a year to rear her children. Afterward, he tried to re-enter the orders. Being a great lover of ritual and much reassured by discipline, he sought out the Trappist Order, perhaps the strictest of all Catholic orders. He claimed he was told by Thomas Merton that he was "perfect for the order." However, his father had a heart attack and "Mother felt I should return home to take care of her." After this, he did not return to a monastery, feeling that at twenty-nine he was too old.

He took a job as a teacher of Latin and Greek in a Catholic boys' school for under-achieving Slav students. While there, he began to experience lancing headaches of such severity that he frequently missed school, because he felt it imperative to get out of the classroom. He drove great distances, on one occasion ending up several hundred miles away. At school, he found that when he wrote words on the blackboard, "they flowed together like liquid." He began to feel that he was being followed, that dynamite had been wired to his automobile ignition, and poison put in his food. His work was disrupted, and he was summarily fired for "irregularity." He was astonished.

He visited home frequently to care for his mother; it was there that he met and became quite emotionally involved with a wealthy widow, "the age of my mother." He loved her rich antiques and secretly began to plan marriage, only to be sharply ridiculed by his sisters. The same old struggle emerged: whether to act for himself or to please the women of his family. To avoid this dilemma, he began to borrow large sums of money from his "fiancée" and escaped from home by taking a plane. He experienced great exultation on "breaking free of the ground." He went several times to Miami and then to Mexico City, where he planned simply to vanish. While there, he applied for a Cuban visa, but it was denied. By now, clear suicidal impulses were consciously obvious to him, as well as his delusions of reference, such as the hostile intent of those who he believed would put a bomb in his car. He ran out of money, wired home for more, and lamely limped back after several weeks.

On his arrival home, the pressures were intense. His fiancée was pressing for marriage or the return of her cash. He knew that his family would laugh at and ridicule him if he married her. At the same time, he became aware of the fact that his mother wasn't just visiting with him; she was "watching me the way people do patients in a psychiatric hospital." He thought, "She thinks I'm sick." He had received two blows: He had been fired for "irregularity," and now his mother saw him "crumbling, when I'm always supposed to be the strong rock, the one everyone leans upon."

He borrowed more money from his fiancée and again flew to Miami determined to kill himself, if only he could overcome his fear of going to Hell. With his last dollars, in a semi-dazed attempt to get farther away, he went by bus to Key West and checked into a hotel. Then came the horrible realization that there was no way "to go farther," it was the "end of the line." His old dream of paralysis came again. As a compromise gesture, he sought to find death by drifting off in a rented boat, but failed miserably. His suicidal drive was too acute to allow him to return to his hotel room on the twentieth floor from where he could dive "right straight to Hell." He called home collect, asked for fifty dollars, and gave his promise to return. Instead, he bought a revolver with the money, with half-formed ideas of suicide, or, preferably, some kind of "shoot-out with the police," in which *they* would kill him. But it seemed to him unfair to put himself on someone else's conscience. He then decided to skyjack a plane to Cuba where Communist Castro would put Catholic him to death, "since I am opposed to Communism." He also had fantasies of destroying Castro and becoming a hero. Now his conscience began to trouble him about jeopardizing the lives of a planeload of people. His solution was to charter a small plane, since he could pay on arrival and would be accompanied by only one other person. Once airborne, he forced the pilot at gunpoint to take him to Cuba.

It should be clearly noted that at the moment of his criminal act, he was one thousand miles from home and separated from all of the people with whom he had troubles. He felt that he had no alternative escape route and that he would otherwise be *obliged to return home in failure again.*

In Cuba, after a check-out by security as a possible CIA agent, he was seen by two psychiatrists. He was freed, set up in a hotel, and finally urged to go by ship to Canada. Interestingly enough, it appeared that the Cuban psychiatrists were caught in a moral dilemma similar to that of the patient. If they returned him to the United States as a "psychotic in search of innocent death," it would be just what he wanted. On the other hand, they didn't want him running loose on the streets, nor did they want the additional expense of him. Their resolution of this problem was to push him off on Canada, hoping that he could receive treatment there. Indeed, the President of Cuba sent him a conciliatory, concerned wire there.

Canada promptly turned him over to the United States.

His dissolution was unbearable. First, Cuba refused to have him killed. Second, he was told that the judge in Miami would be advised that he was sick at the time of commission of the crime, and that he would not be put to death.

During the interview, he was meek, circumspect. His speech was almost inaudible and completely free of profanity. He often used religious terminology. He appeared to be slightly effeminate. He could not laugh at mild sexual levity. He gave the impression of being satiated, admitted a feeling of physical heaviness, and expressed a certain spiritual euphoria. "I am an individual placed on this earth for but a short time, in order to do those things that will give glory to God. Yet I fail, because the world snatched me from the monastery, in which I had been destined to remain. This was my chance of happiness. The rest all have their homes and families, their places in life, but I must resign myself to my fate of being dragged from jail to jail. My country has abandoned me. I pray that God has not done so, for what is left? I live for the day when I shall hear the words, 'Come, my love, my dove, my beautiful one, the winter is over and the rains have ended.' "

He had no criminal record and made no effort to deny his crime, although he denied the ability to commit either murder or rape.

## THE CASE OF ELMER

Elmer was thirty-five and came from a home where the father was an alcoholic and the mother a religious zealot (Church of God). "My father was drunk most of the time. He used to beat Mother and us kids. He used to chase us kids in his truck and try to run over us. He was crazy." His family was socio-economically lower than that of Brian, and their acted-out impulses were more common. For example, during one family fight, a brother older than Elmer stabbed his father in the back in order to protect his mother, who was being choked by his father. (It may be relevant that this wound collapsed one of the father's lungs, subsequently contributing to his dying of pneumonia.)

There were four children: an older brother and sister, and a younger sister. Here, too, the mother won the identification of most of the children, and the feminine dominance of the home was established. "The family split right down the middle with my older brother and Daddy on one side and the rest of us on the other." The girls, as children, involved the patient in all of their games of dolls, in some instances using him as a doll himself. He had many memories of futile rage at being restrained by them for this play.

He also reported dreams of paralysis. "I was afraid a monster would get me. I was all slow motion, my hands and feet were made of lead." Similarly, in sports he was "too clumsy," and "besides, Mother and my sisters sort of had me on their team." He felt the girls were "favored."

Elmer accepted the religious doctrine of his mother wholeheartedly. "At home we prayed a lot and often talked about Hell and what would get us there; all kinds of little things were dangerous. I used to pray that I wouldn't die in my sleep or the monster get me. Heaven sounded pretty good."

During his school years, he "frequently cut out of class just to get outside where I could feel free." He quit school during the tenth grade.

He matured into a quiet "sissy" of such obvious rigidity and morality that, at the time he entered the army, he had never had a date. This innocence and naiveté so offended his fellow recruits that they "bought me a prostitute, but I couldn't do anything. They seemed to think that I put on a lot of airs about not going with women. I didn't dare let them know what I was really feeling, so when we went to the whorehouse, I went up to the girl's room and stayed there awhile. When I came down, I told them I had done it, just as I had told my older brother many years before." (When he had been five years old, his older brother used to try to force him into intercourse with girls. At that time, he went behind the hay bales, only to come out later and report that he "had." His brother wanted to "make me like he was." He meant that his brother wanted to make him "male.")

During military service, he had no dates because he "didn't know how to ask for one." He was quiet, thrifty, and generally envious of the freedom of his bunkmates. "I didn't make much rank during my stay in the service, but I didn't get in any trouble. I knew how to keep my mouth shut."

After discharge from the military, he wandered about alone, envious of the dating of other young men. Finally, he met a very retarded girl who did not frighten him. They went about together for a time "just like the other fellows did," and at last sexual activity began between them.

Almost immediately, he became certain that "people were following" him when he drove about. He was certain that someone was after him, and that perhaps they had wired dynamite to his car. In his fear, he ran to the police and told them to lock him up for safety. Their reply that they weren't "running a hotel" left him depressed. A few hours later, he told them he was planning to bomb the station and shoot everyone in it. The police promptly arranged for his safety in the local state mental hospital.

While in the hospital, he met a seriously ill psychiatric patient who also had epilepsy. She had been hospitalized for twelve years, and Elmer subsequently proposed to her. After both had been released from the hospital, they began to live together, believing marriage to be impossible because of a state law which stated that "an epileptic could not marry." He promptly began to experience the same sort of delusions of being followed and of someone's being "after him," which had occurred after his first sexual experience.

He kept his mouth shut about his suspicions, saved his money from work, and quietly did those prudent things suitable to his situation. He arranged defenses and checks against his enemies and ingratiated himself with his factory supervisor as much as he could. He treasured the belief that he was this man's favorite.

All went along fine, other than the fact that his common-law wife taunted him at home that his penis was "tiny," that he knew nothing about how to use it, and that he didn't take care of her. He was humiliated by these taunts and began to suspect her of infidelity and to check her closely. He found a number of things which, to him, were at first highly suspicious and, finally, absolutely convincing, although in fact, they lacked all substance. For example, on one occasion he found the door unlocked when he came home from work. On other occasions, he was most concerned about cars parked on the block.

During this time, his work apparently suffered. Soon thereafter, he was suddenly, sharply reprimanded by the supervisor whom he believed to be his best friend. He was amazed by this further evidence of infidelity and began to plot the murder of this man, as well as shooting up "some of those people" who were following him. He first bought a pistol to carry out his purpose, but later settled on a knife as being somehow more suitable, so he made one from an old file.

Much disturbed by his feelings, he vacillated for weeks between the intention to kill and the wish to make up. He was dissatisfied with his plans for mass murder because it was "the good people" who were persecuting him for his sexual sins. He hated the thought of killing them, since there were so many of them. During this time, he and his common-law wife drove about a great deal in his car, and he watched the rear view mirror closely.

He felt sure he had developed skin cancer as a result of his sexual sin. His skin "stank," and he felt that the pores at the hair roots had opened into gaping spaces from which the evil odor came. He went to a physician, but since the doctor belonged to the "good people," he wouldn't cure him. Also, the doctor began to hint to the patient that his problems were mental, and that he should go to the hospital. He became even more fearful and decided that only Russia, which belonged to the Devil, would treat his disease. Therefore, he traveled to Washington and applied for a visa to Russia, in order to obtain treatment. Apparently, the Russians were doubtful about him, and there were inexplicable delays in his receiving the necessary documents. Like Brian, he was far from home, stymied in his wish to escape from the United States, and faced with having to return home once again as a failure.

He decided to go to Cuba without the formalities. He bought a return ticket to his hometown, and, using his gun, he demanded to be flown to Cuba. He was very puzzled by the amiability and compliance of the crew, and he was softening under their kindness, until they offered to let him sit in a pilot's seat. Instantly, he figured that it was "rigged to a trap door and that they would dump me." He stiffened and regained control of his feelings and the situation. Their continued kindness and affability, however, troubled him, and at last he put his gun down.

Interestingly, he was miraculously "cured" of his skin cancer in Dade County Jail by a bowl of soup he received from the warden.

During the interview, he made no attempt to justify his crime. He obviously felt he had not sinned against God, but had committed only a secular crime. He was meek and appeared to be effeminate, both physically and in his speech. He didn't smoke, drink, or curse. He used righteous platitudes and indicated his desire to serve in the ministry.—After Elmer left the room, an interesting thing happened. A particularly sensitive staff member softly hummed, then sang the line, "Oh, if I had the wings of an angel. . . ."

During my training in Chicago, the individuals who influenced me most were Franz Alexander and Lionel Blitzsten. Alexander had searched to discover what one sufferer of a certain disease had in common with a comparable sufferer. In studying the cases of Brian and Elmer, we had employed similar common profiles to visualize commonalities of function between them.

Such a method of study acts in sharp contrast to that of Blitzsten, who, in his meticulous search for that which was unique and individual about one person, interviewed in depth. In the present study, we were in the situation of having interviewed in depth, using the technique of Blitzsten, with a resultant opportunity to apply the method of Alexander to the interview material.

# II
# First Step Toward a Theory

Our discussion following the interviews indicated, in a veiled way, that some cherished dogmas may have been threatened and questions raised that were not easily answerable along Freudian lines. In particular, the questions bore on the theory of reality formation and seemed to suggest that the period of infancy, as characterized by Freud, may be preceded by some sort of universal experience that had been overlooked.

To me, the actions of these two men were symbolic and recalled the determination of children to walk or skate at an age when they had not yet become afflicted with the curse of self-consciousness and shame. The skyjackers seemed intent to stand on their own feet, to be men, to face their God, and to arise from this planet to the other more pleasing place.

My plane ride back to Dallas was pleasant. I was thinking about the exultant feelings of both men and their response to *breaking free from the ground.* I thought about the floating ecstasy, of their sensations of being *so high,* and of the earth's being *so tiny* and *so far away.* To them, it was as if in the act of flight, they had achieved their manhood. (As it later developed, and was even much more germane, they had re-achieved their personhood.) Why, I wondered, should flight, with its implied sense of freedom, both specific and symbolic, be the ultimate expression of self-hood for them? The Freudian approach through the sexualized relevance of this material offered a ready explanation, but somehow it lacked adequate applicability for us to "feel right" about its theoretical appropriateness in these cases.

In clinical medicine, a group of symptoms, regularly occurring together as being characteristic of a specific process, are called a "syndrome." I began to think in terms of a syndrome, and I began to draw a common profile. I listed the close similarities between the two, with the thought in mind that, if it were to become possible to interview others later on, it would be interesting to see how closely these early parameters contained them.

The following profile emerged:

1. The fathers of both were violent, alcoholic, and abusive to women—as witnessed by them in childhood.
2. Both mothers were religious zealots.
3. The internal structure of both families created sharp conflicts. Each man came to believe that mother was "good" and associated with God, whereas father was "bad" and associated with the Devil.
4. Both had sisters two years younger than themselves.
5. By the end of the fifth year of life, both had come to accept the mother's wish that they "protect the honor of their sisters" and "help them get fixed in life."
6. Both related recurring dreams, beginning at age five, which involved being paralyzed and unable to rise, and which closely resembled their daytime sense of bodily heaviness.
7. Both experienced mild neuromuscular incapacity, which largely excluded them from play with peers.
8. Between age five and eight, both rejected the "bad-devil father" from their conscious identification.
9. Both identified with the maternal family values.
10. Both suppressed envy of the natural closeness between the mother and sisters.
11. By age eight, both were extremely religious, accepting Christ as their Saviour. Both lived in fear of Hell and hope of Heaven.
12. Both developed slow, plodding personalities.
13. By adolescence, both were severely shy.
14. In adolescence, both were loners.
15. At college age, neither dated and—remarkably— accounted for it in identical words: "I didn't know how to ask."

16. By age thirty, both felt themselves to be complete failures.
17. Neither had negative political attitudes toward the United States.
18. Both were nationalistic and had no wish to humiliate this nation. They had no admiration for the Communist system.
19. Both felt personally "evil" and feared the "good people."
20. Neither had any grudge against airlines.
21. In moments of anxiety, both drove automobiles for long distances to relieve tension.
22. Neither had experienced satisfactory sexual relationships.
23. In early manhood, both spent a period of considerable time being secluded from the world—one in a monastery, the other in a mental hospital.
24. Both wished to serve in the ministry.
25. Neither smoked nor drank.
26. Neither had a criminal record.
27. Both watched television for extended periods in an effort to escape reality.
28. Both experienced the loss, partial or total, of the father, several years prior to their crime.
29. Shortly before skyjacking, both had been astonished at being "let down" by an authoritative male who, they strongly believed, had been "on their side."
30. Shortly before skyjacking, both began to experience sustained humiliation by the important women in their lives.
31. Each experienced strong murderous impulses toward the above figures, *or others,* as a consequence of this rage and frustration.
32. During this agitated period, each drove or flew great distances to escape momentarily from the fear of these explosive feelings.
33. Each experienced dissociative episodes involving confusion of time and distance. Each was often directionally disoriented.
34. Both experienced fears of being followed and of somebody's being "against them."

35. Each believed that his car had been boobytrapped, or his food poisoned.

36. In both, the above fears arose in connection with sexual activity.

37. Both struggled in a conflict over the commission of murder/suicide and sought morally more acceptable acts.

38. Both made applications to enter Communist countries, with the intention of permanent escape from conflicts.

39. Each experienced a sense of being "at the end of the rope" and left home by plane to accomplish the above. At his destination, each failed.

40. In the final, futile moment, both were alone and a long distance from home.

41. Both carried newly purchased guns, and neither had previous gun experience to speak of. The guns were loaded, and they were jumpily determined to use them "if need be."

42. Each was resigned to "flip the coin" to decide on a way to die, be executed, or escape (suicidal substitutes without personal responsibility).

43. Both attempted capture of an airplane in order to direct it to Cuba.

44. Neither used profanity.

45. Both spoke in righteous platitudes.

46. Both spoke so softly as to be almost inaudible, in spite of the aid of a microphone.

47. Both used mildly effeminate gestures.

48. Both made occasional feminine choice of words and images.

49. Neither was able to laugh at mild sexual levity.

50. Neither appeared to make even a mild effort to deny his crime or to excuse it.

51. Both had experienced physical sensations in which their bodies felt heavier than usual, although their heads felt lighter.

52. Both seemed emotionally spent in the fashion of one who has been satiated by a large meal or by sexual activity. They described this state as though it were a mild feeling of euphoria.

53. Each man stated suicide would be easy for him, murder possible, but rape "unthinkable."

There were the following differences between them:

1. One was more murderous than suicidal, the other more suicidal than murderous.
2. Although both were virtual celibates, the more murderous one took a common-law wife choosing a physically and mentally ill woman, whom he was incapable of pleasing.
3. One succeeded in reaching Cuba (the more suicidal one), the other lost his nerve during his attempt.

From the point of view of psychiatry, there was nothing particularly unusual about the progression of the case histories. In fact, the first attempt to see the outlines of a syndrome was rendered impossible by the fact that there must have been many thousands of men in this country with such traits in common.

On the other hand, there had been only fifty skyjackings over an eight-year period in the United States and Central America, in a total population of almost 300 million. Eight years is expressible as 864 billion man-days, within which span, fifty skyjackings had occurred. Thus, each of these two men represented an incidence of one in six million, yet each was psychologically, historically, and legally astoundingly like the other.

After much thought, I realized that carrying this sort of statistical analysis to a logical conclusion would yield unacceptable results, and that, therefore, there must be additional factors that influenced these two men at the time of the commission of their crimes. Men with life histories of their type, who manifest similar symptoms, generally never exhibit overt criminal activity. A few commit rape, or murder and rape, but skyjackings are very few and far between.

My attention now turned to my distinct impression of the coexistence of "dual realities" in the two men, which struck me as being so firmy intertwined as to be indistinguishable. But in the process of skyjacking, the realities had become, momentarily, detached and identifiable and, in that moment, aspects of each reality also became capable of symbolic substitution between themselves.

The two "realities" were: (1) physical attraction of mass for mass, which in its aggregate is called "gravity"; this reality is *physical* and basic; (2) emotional attraction of human being for human being, which in its aggregate is called "social compact"; this reality is *human* and basic. If the force of physical attraction (gravity) cohesively holds the earth together in its physical structure, so too does the force of emotional attraction (compact) cohesively hold society together in its social structure. Could it be possible that the latter fact (compact) is patterned upon the former fact (gravity), and could, indeed, even be its prerequisite?

For the human infant in the beginning, it is undoubtedly true that one of the most evident benefits of "belonging to the human race" is that he can be *moved about by the adults in his surroundings.* Before he has learned to move himself about, he learns to cry or to stretch out his arms in order to bring others to him, because *they can defeat the gravity which binds him to his position.* Perhaps motion of any kind seems valuable and might lead to a desire to emulate the figure who seems most able to defy the physical environment—in most cases, the father.[1] Thus, the first understanding for the infant would be the "power" of gravity itself, and the second the "power" of the adult who could defeat gravity physically. Later, as he learned the "power" of the ethical system which could defeat both gravity and the father's physical power, he would achieve the ultimate in controlling his environment. Obedience to the social compact would be seen as essential to participation in this highest power.

The skyjacker's ultimate challenge appeared to lie in his simultaneous defiance of *both* realities. Flight is the defiance of physical gravity, murder/suicide the defiance of emotional gravity. In the process, he set himself against the total environment (reality) at the risk of death.

In one abrupt action, in the wild hope of breaking his emotional chains in order to "live," each of these men broke both gravitational and social ties. In psychiatric terms, the id denied the superego at the price of possible death. Starkly manifest here is the no-

---

[1] Obviously, babies discover Mother before they do Father. However, I have reason to state the proposition thusly, which is clarified in Chapter VII.

tion that if a man would fully live, he can do so only if he gambles his person, his life, and his status; just as when the infant first dares to stand in the "unknown" of vertical posture, he must assume not only the load of a heavy burden, but the possibility of falling and being destroyed. We might all well agree with Auden's proposal:

> Let us honor, if we can
> The vertical man.

The notion that man patterns the structure of his institutions after his ego, which itself is derived from his needs, is perfectly reasonable. It has long been accepted that the ego is the internal representation of man's capacities created to gratify the id. At the same time that Freud created the concept, "Where id was, there shall ego be," he split off the superego. By claiming that the super-ego was a derivative of the ego, he created a paradox that has produced continuous confusion, for there emerged from this concept the image of an ego constantly at war with its own derivative. This image contains an illogicality. Consequently, the superego is less and less frequently viewed as an operational concept, which is unfortunate.

If one were to accept Freud's understanding as a basis for analysis of these two cases, then one would assume that id derivatives (actions) were simultaneously defying gravity (physical environment) and the superego (human environment), because each was bent upon his own destruction through the defiance of physical and human law (the realities in which one lives). This assumption would be incorrect. The wish to live is indomitable and denies mortality. What seems more likely is that an ancient introjected figure (the father), vested with much primary pre-logical thinking, re-emerged in the imagination of these men at a desperate juncture in their lives, defying now as it had seemed to defy before, all the rules of social and environmental reality in its determination to live.

The inevitable consequence of the classical theoretical considerations, in which the spark of life turns upon itself, intending its own self-destruction, is illogical. The spark of life can be intent only upon its own survival and expression. It is the environment that indifferently destroys life, even as it momentarily supports it. In the patients at hand, I viewed their defiance of both gravity and the social compact, and their recognition that their defiance might well culminate in the termination of their lives, as evidence of a conflict between the individual (id-ego) and the internalized mental representative (gravity-superego) of the environment itself. These individuals were pitting their lives against the mental representatives of both realities.

This conclusion denied that the superego was a derivative of the ego and postulated for it a separate origin, namely, that it is the mental derivative of a *separate force,* that force being gravity. With this conclusion, several dualities were created which did not lead to the paradoxes of the classical theory. Since the concept had a comfortable logic to it, and since I was unaware of the "heresy" and complications involved, I simply assumed that gravity was important, and that it had its own mental representative in the human personality.

In such a view, the drive of the id would be totally upward and the drive of gravity totally downward. As such, if ego gratification lay in the direction of "up," and if superego gratification lay in the direction of "down," one might readily conceive a vertical gradient extending between these two infinities. Such a gradient would be bisected in the middle by a line representative of a horizon. Then, if one were to imagine individuals (as reflected in body, mood, status, etc.) on the gradient, most people, most of the time, would be placed at the intersection of the vertical and the horizontal. From moment to moment, the image each has of his own person might rise or fall so that he might describe himself as being momentarily high or low.

When one considers the life situation of these men immediately prior to the crime on such a gradient, it would appear as if their image has been appreciably below the horizontal for years and has most recently been driven downward at an extremely precipitous rate toward a point of non-existence. They were falling faster and faster. It was apparent in their downward course that they had utilized all manner of defenses: physical movement, physical flight, isolation, pain, dissociation, and depression, all in unsuccessful attempts to stop the downward movement. In their final symbolic act, by "standing up" and by "threatening with force," *they intended to move the image of their own person vertically up the axis.* It appeared the experience would be physical, social, and spiritual at one and the same moment.

Such a view contained within it elements of psychiatric "heresy," but I reconciled myself with the thought that, at the time of the evolution of Freud's theory, man's movement was basically still restricted to the limits of his own physical neuromuscular system. Man was only beginning to defy earth's gravity in flight, and he had not learned to create centrifugal gravity through the technologies made possible by reciprocating engines, jets, or rockets. In effect, what I had postulated might well be considered as one result of an *"age of flight" of man's nature.* As the pre-Freudian period was unable to expose the presence of an unconscious because of hypocrisy and taboos, so Freud's age was unable to recognize fully the import of gravity to the development of the human personality.

This thought brought to mind the similarity between these cases and the symbolic meaning of the space program, through which man, in his infinitely id-ish way, taxed the capacities of his ego to rape the heavens. In its ultimate form, man intends to project his own seed into the universe, whether she is willing for him to do so or not, and in direct defiance of gravity. In the period since 1957, much of American man's national interest, personal ambition, dreams, and his conception of his own person has been wrapped up in the space program. In 1961, the first fruit of the program was harvested. This led me to speculate that in stealing aircraft in that same year, downtrodden, helpless misfits were unconsciously attempting to identify themselves with an astronaut (a space rapist), rising to the heavens of elation from the hell of their own despair. They had come to a time in life in which they could no longer bridge the gap between their knowledge and the mysteries by an act of faith, through which they had been able to transcend self previously. For their loss of psychic transcendence, they substituted physical transcendence in an aircraft, in search of a new homeostasis.

## PSYCHOLOGICAL RAPE

The concept of rape, in a non-genital context, involving these two skyjackers had been forced upon us by a third patient we had seen the same day. He brought to mind Harry Stack Sullivan, who wrote, "Everyone is much more simply human than otherwise." [2] He meant to say that cultural differences aside, there are certain events which so mold us that, even in an alien and non-verbal situation, there are knowledges and humors which can be interchanged between people of disparate origins in spite of language and reality barriers.

This man had been added to our interview list because he had been such a problem to the prison management. He was in prison for mail fraud and passport irregularities. He had nearly broken the spirit of his jailers. He claimed that he had been excluded from the practice of his religion. He had brought federal suit for his privileges, and he had won. He was preparing for another fight, in which he planned to force the prison to maintain a special kitchen for himself alone! The feelings of prisoner and staff were that he would whip them since "God was on his side." He was "standing up" to the establishment.

He was a peculiar little man, half-shaven with a patchy beard. (It turned out that a guard had tried to shear him with scissors because the guard had reacted to the arrogance of the prisoner.) When he entered the consultation room, he stood for a time and sought out every eye at the interview table. I opened the interview by asking him why he had studied the group so closely. His reply began, "The Book says . . . ," and its substance was a long religious quotation regarding looking one's examiners in the eye. In an emotional sense, he brought me sharply up against the realization that he and I lived in different worlds. His intimation was that his world was the better and *higher* one, and throughout the interview we teetered along the perilous rim between our two worlds. Each word he spoke, every movement he made, and every thought he had

2 Henry Stack Sullivan, *The Interpersonal Theory of Psychiatry* (New York: W. W. Norton & Co., 1953), p. 33.

were in some sense required by his religion. His every action was controlled and required by that religion and if, by chance, I was displeased with him, it mattered little to him, for I was both ignorant and a sinner. It further appeared that, if his actions displeased the secular authorities, it was their problem because they were not recognized by his religious authority. As this line of fact and fiction emerged, it became beautifully clear that he had indeed been guilty of the statutory crimes attributed to him, but these were not weighing on his conscience since the actions themselves had been performed for the benefit of his religious cause and therefore were, as in the other two cases, the expression of a deep religious loyalty to an authority that stood over and against the secular law.

He was less acutely ill than the two skyjackers and had been less violent in his crime. He, unlike the other two, had just steadily "screwed" the world for God. That word "screwed" seemed somehow to fit his actions perfectly. In his behavior in the interview, in his relationship to the prison, and, I'm sure, in his interpersonal relationships before his arrest, he had just plain "screwed" the world with his piety, even over its pitiful cries for mercy.

This thought tickled me more than a little, because in its own way it described so well what he had attempted to do all through his interview, and it fitted exactly the phrase used by the "hip generation" when they feel someone is trying to force values into their heads that are at variance with those they hold at the moment. At such times, they say the speaker is trying to "mind-fuck them." They protest, as if it were rape. In more confused moments, they may express the image as that of a hard penis being thrust into their heads. Symbolically, to force one's will upon another, over his protest, is in itself a form of *rape*. And the more I reflected upon it, the more clearly I saw that each of the men was busy at his rape in his own way. In point of fact, it was related to the fact that the fellow recruits of the second skyjacker had become so tired after a few days of being "shafted" by his piety that they had passed the hat to buy him a whore. They said, by this action, "Do it to her in an honest and human way and come down from your holy cloud from which we keep getting the shaft."

# III

# False Starts

Having formulated the hypotheses about the environmental and social drives to which the two skyjackers might have been responding, it seemed a good idea to examine the men a second time.

At the second interview, Brian stated that "a fantasy, or whatever it was," had been with him continuously since the first interview. His thoughts had centered on his father: his father's age, his occupation, his political connections, his power, and the notion that his father was wealthy. He had also experienced an intense feeling that his own actions had been in some way ordained by the gods, and at the same moment he felt that he was tricking the Devil when he felt that his death was near. It was clear from his remarks that he was trying to decide who his father was, whether his father was God or the Devil. He was trying to settle for himself the question, "To whom do I belong?"

He further stated that he had always felt that his life was frenzied, as though he were opposed by some irresistible force that was trying to pull him down into nothingness. He said that he had made efforts lately to force himself to participate in life with others. As one manifestation of his struggle "upward," he had recently tried to avoid his tendency to escape from life through television, which had been his principal activity during the onset of his illness. He further stated that he had no explanation for the fact that after the first interview his headaches had gone away and not returned. Beyond this point the interview slid effortlessly into a discussion of mankind's general state, of his sense of despair, and of his need for a feeling of transcendence. He stated that, were it not for the sense of elation and elevation which he had experienced when thinking of Christ, life would be for him most unbearable physically. He was particularly impressed by the belief that Jesus had walked on the water and that he had risen from the dead. His own faith was based on these two beliefs. Further questioning elicited from him direct, associative connections between his feelings in regard to these miraculous events and some of his own sensations experienced in connection with the United States space effort. In particular, he provided us with vivid descriptions of his exultant, excited feelings as he watched the astronauts on television moving about weightlessly inside the space capsule and performing minor gymnastic miracles.

He spoke then of his youthful interest in learning to fly. He had found it impossible to realize his ambition because of financial and physical reasons, but he still had a sizable, albeit gentle, envy of men who were able to fly, even in mundane, motor-driven craft. This discussion led on to further description of the intense emotional pleasure he derived from the flights he had made. He told of the excitement of chartering a plane. It was obvious that this form of physical movement and of technological advance was, for him, an almost specific resolution of an unbearable gravito-inertial awareness.

He explained further that he had been examined by a psychiatrist while in the Cuban prison because of the headaches he was experiencing, and that he had been given a tranquilizer. The medication affected him severely. He became quite dizzy and experienced acute vertigo. He believed then that the Cubans were poisoning his food. Later, he went to a nearby clinic at the University of Havana and was seen by a young Army doctor who treated him with courtesy and discontinued the medication. He found upon his return to the States that the tranquilizers given him in the course of his hospitalization still seemed to produce unusual sensitivity. Many were specifically contraindicated because of their tendency to disturb his equilibrium.

Elmer, too, had been an active viewer of television in his cramped, schizophrenic living style. It was his tendency, if he was not out driving in his car, to stay close by home in order to watch television. He had, with great avidity, followed the proceedings of the space effort. His feelings about the transcendent and the elevating sensation he experienced by virtue of his belief in Christ were described to us in almost identical, physical terms.

During the interview, his capacity for recall of various events within the space program turned out to be unusually high. In a general sense, his recall in other areas was not as acute. It was also observed during the discussions of the space program that he experienced a great deal of excitement and moved about more in his chair, rocking forward and backward, as if, in some way, providing himself with a physical solace for the restrictions of prison life.

The supra-gravitational nature of God and of the two primary miracles of Christ involving this function were also of particular importance to him. His faith rested on them, and from them flowed his transcendental sense of goodness and his religious preoccupation. He clearly stated that his personal feelings of self-acceptance at such moments were richly rewarding and constituted total relief from the usual heavy, weighty, dirty, evil feelings that he experienced about himself when he stopped to consider his actual position in life, and particularly his relationship with his wife.

Following these interviews, I felt it was essential to communicate such information as I had at that time both to the airline industry and to the Department of Justice. (The federal prison system does not have a medical corps of its own, and its medical needs are attended to by the United States Public Health Service. Thus, while I was organizationally attached to the Public Health Service, I was also functionally working for the Department of Justice.)

The material was dispatched to the Department through an intermediary and, after a long time had gone by with no response, I called to inquire and was informed that the record had been given to the Assistant Attorney General in charge of prosecution. Since I had known him vaguely when he was District Attorney in Dallas, it seemed like a reasonable assumption that we could talk. When I called him directly, his opening remark was, "Are you opposed to the death penalty?" Although this question was irrelevant at this point, I answered it, only to be asked, "Have you ever spoken out in public against the death penalty?" I replied that I never have in a speech, nor have I ever been active in any organization associated with that cause, but it was not impossible that I might have responded at some time to a question with a reply that expressed doubt about the value of such a penalty. Beyond that point, the interview was non-productive, and it was made clear to me that if I came to Washington, no one in his department would have the time to sit with me for a fuller discussion of the case material.

At this juncture, it appeared that I had seen all skyjackers who would be made available through the federal prison system. Clearly, the principal source of more clinical material was Cuba. If I was to extend the study, it would be imperative to get at it.

Since I was without connections that might have helped me to get to Cuba, I did two things. First, I wrote an article for a national medical journal about the findings to date in the two cases. I hoped, by this means, to communicate with the Cuban medical community in order to gain their cooperation. Second, I attempted to win possible cooperation from the airline industry, and after some false starts I was told to contact the Washington office of the Air Transport Association. They agreed to put forth their best efforts to facilitate a trip to Cuba, but pointed out that my plans might come into conflict with those of the Federal Aviation Agency, which had only recently been assigned the responsibility for the study and control of skyjacking. It was proposed that I clear my plans with the FAA. After a number of maddening and time-wasting attempts had been completed, I accomplished two minor feats. First, I obtained a record of all data relative to the history of skyjacking insofar as the FAA was cognizant of it. Second, I secured agreement that, if the data on the incidence of skyjacking revealed a close relationship to my hypothetical tenets, then a meeting would be held shortly thereafter between the FAA, the State Department, the Air Transport Association, and myself.

The historical data received from the FAA follows:

In 1961, there were three successful and two unsuccessful hijackings of U.S. airplanes. In 1962, there was one successful hijacking, which was the only one attempted. No hijackings were attempted in 1963. In 1964, there was one successful hijacking. In 1965, there were three attempted hijackings, all of them unsuccessful. In 1966, there were none attempted. In November, 1967, there was one successful hijacking attempt. In the first half of 1968, there were four hijackings and about fifteen more during the second half of 1968. There has been an increasing number of them this year. The frequency curve for foreign hijackings paralleled that of the domestic rate. Both rates have been increasing in the past year or so at an exponential rate.[1]

I had already gathered the available information about manned space flights, and now I found that the immediate correlation between the commencement of space activity and the commencement of the skyjacking was striking. (See graph.) It was decided to have our Washington meeting.

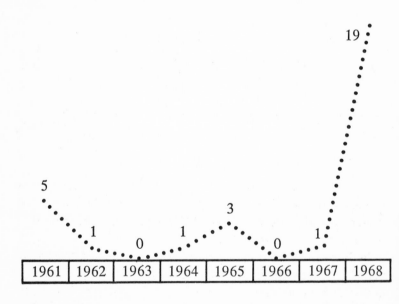

This simple graph reflects the fact that the principal years of skyjacking were 1961, 1965, and 1968. These same years repre-

[1] Personal communication—these data were supplied by John G. Dailey, Ph.D., Chief of Psychology Staff, Washington, D.C., February 12, 1969.

sented the years of maturation of the Mercury, Gemini, and Apollo series in our space program. Ordinarily, the Apollo series would have occurred in 1969, but President Johnson accelerated the program. Even so, as it turned out, the principal "pulse" of the skyjack effort covered a period of roughly July, 1968, to July, 1969.

If it were true that the sudden onset of skyjacking in the United States had occurred in the same year as the beginning of our space effort, it seemed wise to look more closely at that year to see what specific relationship, if any, might exist between the two sets of events.

A review of newspapers for the year yielded dates on both sky-jacking and manned space flight. In graphic form, it looked like this:

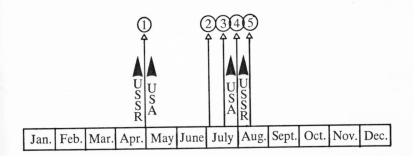

The first skyjacker rose in the five-day period between the first U.S.S.R and first U.S.A. effort. The fourth man did the same in the five-day period between the second U.S.A. and U.S.S.R. shots. The others were tightly clustered nearby.

Both sets of events occurred close together in about a ninety-day period. The newspapers at the time were particularly interesting in that, at both the start and finish of the ninety-day period, a single front page would include an article on a space shot just recently completed, a skyjacking on the day of issuance, and a space shot in countdown! The articles even touched each other. Like the staff man who hummed, "Oh, if I had the wings of an angel," the compositor of this page knew more than he knew he knew.

While en route to the Washington meeting, it struck me that the apparent relationship was perilously neat and tidy. There had been many unmanned space vehicles extruded into space in the years preceding manned flights. If manned flight could produce such a sudden upsurge, there surely must have been some kind of antecedent behavior that had changed and transmuted itself into this one. The data did not suggest what it might have been.

## FIRST WASHINGTON TRIP

The conduct of the participants was revealing to observe. The State Department men were open, eager, and willing to talk. They were cooperative and supplied me with a great deal of data. They promised their cooperation in clearing my passport for Cuba, and I felt that they were open to anything else that they thought might work. The representative of the Air Transport Association gradually withdrew from participating in the meeting. This became obvious after I overstated some psychoanalytic interpretations of the nature of flight, namely, that it possibly had aggressive sexual connotations and that skyjacking might be described as a form of rape. Toward the end of the meeting, he assured me, with some vehemence, that when he took flight training at Kelly Field he was "sure as heck not indirectly raping a woman by any activities on the plane." After the meeting, being a forthright man, he said, "Now, look, Doctor, we're not interested in this thing beyond this point, and we drop any further interest in it. I can't say to you, 'It was interesting.' That's what you say to the preacher when you weren't listening. I know, in fact, something happened here today, but I don't want to know what it was."

The response of the FAA was guarded and hesitant. For some time, I thought that they might have spotted some inadequacy in my study, but later I realized that, as new as they were in the game and with as little data as they had at the time, they could hardly take a position other than one of guarded hesitance. With a modicum of recollection, I would have recalled the fact that they had just been assigned the problem, after it had lain for many years with a pilots' group. It became quite clear, when I recalled the chain of early telephone calls which had led to their office.

In one call, I spoke with the Miami pilot in charge of the investigation. After perhaps a week's delay, because of the numerous meetings this man was attending in his capacity as an expert, we finally talked, and I attempted to lay out a little of the material at hand. His reply was, "My God, Doc, I don't know what to do about all that. I'm a pilot and airplanes is all I know." That he had been in charge of the investigation had a certain kind of logic, when you consider that the wounded party in a skyjacking is an airplane. However, when one considers the fact that the crime was perpetrated by a human being, responding to thoughts and emotions, it made little sense.

Prior to leaving Washington, I dropped by the Czechoslovak Embassy in order to prepare an application for a Cuban visa. For quite some time, there was no word, and ultimately it was declined.

## AFTER WASHINGTON

On the way to Washington, I had drawn quite a list of questions to ask concerning the knowledge of the importance of different social factors, emotionally moving events, and sociology. It might help to know the interrelatedness of certain wave-types of human behavior. Essentially, the questions to be posed were like these: What sort of tools does the government have with which to measure the "internal temperature" of a population? Were there "probes" by means of which one could actually measure the level of unrest as shown by the movement of the citizenry within the body politic? (Certain *rates* of activity must result in a certain amount of odd behavior.) Was there a relationship between the civil unrest that had stirred the South at about the same period and the subsequent burnings of cities and campus revolts? It is now clear that, not only the FAA, but *no agency* within the government actually has knowledge of this kind. There are no available standards of measurement by which to probe into the living, moving characteristics of society.

At that point, I decided to attempt to get permission to study skyjackers who had failed to get to Cuba. It appeared that the Dade County jail in Florida happened to have six untried offenders all at one time. We set about getting clearance to examine them. My first contact with a federal judge in Miami was delightful. He said, "Why sure, young fellow, you come on down here and see what you can find." He even agreed to check with the other occupants of that federal district to see if they had any other cases which might be seen.

A few hours after this pleasant conversation, the irate voice of the *Chief Judge* of the district brought me back to reality. He wanted to know why I had spoken with an underling rather than himself, and what the hell I was up to. His chief fear seemed to be that an outsider might expose the foul conditions of the Dade County jail system, where four men are housed in facilities designed for one. He also seemed fearful that the federal bench could not manage to get the cooperation from the county people who ran the jails to move the prisoners around for interview. After a thorough explanation that I was not a bleeding heart bent on a jail exposé, he calmed down and agreed to permit me to come, provided that "it all be in writing." I agreed to send him a wire.

Before I could dispatch it, the good judge was back on the phone to announce that the study was "off." He had spoken with "Washington" and had been informed that the study would "violate the prisoners' constitutional rights." (See Chapter VIII.)

I managed to examine most of the prisoners later, after they were convicted, even though they were scattered all over the nation in different prisons, which required more travel, more time, more expense.

Having failed once to enter either Cuba or Dade County, I tried the Cubans later, through their Mexico Consul. They have a brooding, fortresslike structure in the suburbs of Mexico City. As had previously been agreed with the U.S. Department of State, full disclosure of findings was made. We had language problems, but we made do. The Consul's only real interest, however, was in my correspondence with the Czechoslovaks and theirs with me. (Probably allies are like that; they just like to check upon one another every now and then.) He asked if he could borrow the letters for quick reproduction. Since there was nothing wrong with that, it was easy to agree. A few moments later a clerk informed us that "the machine, she is broke." He agreed the letters would be returned at a later date. I have yet to see them.

Later, the Consul apologized for the "slovenly ways of his Czechoslavak allies in the handling of the visa." He asked me to fill out a new request. In this instance, it only required five months for the request to be declined.

# IV

# Reinforcements and Complications

Shortly after this series of exercises in futility, I was informed by the FAA Psychiatric Consultant that he just remembered the name of a man who had some years earlier failed in his skyjacking effort, was subsequently tried and sentenced to prison, and was free by this time. He thought that I might be able to examine the man, and we located him through official records. The man was contacted and willingly agreed to come to Dallas for study, with the understanding that such a study might aid in gaining an understanding of the phenomenon.

I had a tape recorder by then, and it was used to record my interview with the visiting skyjacker, as with all subsequent cases.

This is an appropriate juncture to point out that in the case histories that follow, the subjects will speak for themselves in direct quotations from tapes of the interviews, as much as space and other overriding factors allow. Where the procedure is repetitive or disjointed, I will summarize what was said. Pseudonyms are employed throughout.

As far as it was possible to do so, personal data have been altered to preclude identification. When the tape recorder was set up, each subject was told that his case material would be used in an effort to illuminate the problem. None refused and, as previously noted, each expressed the hope that "his interview" might contribute something to the study.

My comments that follow the case histories reflect, as objectively as possible, only the contents of the material from which they were derived. The quotations have not been edited in any way. I have not attempted to interpret "in depth" either the subjects' understanding of what they have said or what they have done. I have tried to stand back and view in perspective such common factors in their feeling and behavior as may have emerged.

I have largely avoided the use of psychiatric terminology and made no effort to distinguish between psychotic and neurotic subjects. It really makes no difference. The impulse, with its employed symbolism, is unconscious in either case, and the ego is inadequate to hold it in check.

## THE CASE OF BOB

Bob was white, age twenty. He came from an intact family and had one brother two years older than himself and one sister two years younger.

His father was an engineer and once held an important job. Later, he became less active in a job which seems to have been less important and only part-time. He was from Utah and was a Mormon. He was an aggressive, overpowering, individual, who completely subjugated his wife and children. He was very hostile to his wife and very critical as well. He did not drink because of his religion.

The mother was a Christian Scientist. Bob said, "She believes all of it." The father, however, did not allow her to attend church often. She did manage to send the children to a Presbyterian Sunday School every week, although "she didn't dare face Dad and go herself." She worked as a full-time secretary. Neither she nor the father was home during the day. She leaned heavily on the patient for emotional gratification, but was never able to take his side in a father-son dispute.

That patient's earliest memories were of seeing his newborn sister. His mother taught him to protect his little sister and take care of her. He, his mother, and sister "hung together pretty close." He was clearly female-dominated. He often felt obliged to protect his little sister from his brother's friends at his mother's request. He strongly believed her to be favored.

He reported childhood dreams of something coming toward him and being unable to move. "Nothing would happen, my body would not respond. I felt like I weighed ten tons." Similar dreams involving slow motion and paralysis extended into the present times. He had much the same feelings in sports and rarely participated. He had few friends. He added, "Besides, it seemed to me the other guys were dirty, both in their bodies which were unclean, and in the bad talk they used. They poked fun at me for my religious convictions." For these same reasons, he never became a Scout like his brother. He was always a good child, saying of himself, "At eight I learned the bad words, and at nine I abandoned them." He remembered frequent car sickness at age five.

His hobby was collecting things. "I had a collection of key chains, stamps, coins, rocks, broken watches, every letter and card I had ever received, and a clipping book of all the astronauts' activities." He would very much like to be one. He also had a box full of hundreds of balls from ballpoint pens, which he kept in the box with a magnet. "Giving up anything gave me a great feeling of sacrifice and a sharp sense of loss."

The one physical activity in which he participated was long-distance running. He had the self-discipline for distance, but he could not make the anti-narcissistic drive necessary for sprints. He was basically a loner. There was little interaction between himself and his peers, siblings, or his father. The only basis for communication between father and son was intellectual. He established a straight "A" average early in his school life in an attempt to please his father. Apparently, status, involving intellectual achievements, was important to his father. The boy had been expected to graduate at the end of his junior year in high school by taking summer courses for credit. This left him little time for any activity other than studying.

Bob never dated. "Because I was much too shy and timid to ask a girl." He felt uncomfortable when a girl was physically near him and hoped this would never occur when his parents were around, feeling that they might tease him. Although he ran for Student Council in his high school for two successive years, he was defeated both times. This contributed to a growing sense of failure, caused primarily by the progressive difficulty of his academic work and the arduous task of maintaining his straight "A" average. Shortly before his attempted skyjacking, he got a "C" in a physics course. He had taken the course at his father's insistence (once again his mother had failed to come to his aid), and he greatly feared paternal rejection as a result of the low mark. He generally spent many hours studying. During that semester he was very depressed and often "felt like a sleepwalker." He was aware of strong hostile and destructive feelings toward his parents for "pushing me to failure." He felt great guilt about this until the feelings were transferred to Castro.

Bob was patriotic. The skyjacking was merely a means of getting to Cuba; once there, he planned either to help destroy the Communist government by aiding guerrilla efforts to kill the Communist leaders, or to allow himself to be martyred so that the publicity might bring the necessity of immediate action in Cuba to the attention of the American public. He believed there was a great urgency about the Cuban situation, owing to Cuba's proximity to the United States, and hoped by his personal acts to dramatize the situation. In his high school he was the only Goldwater supporter and was ridiculed for it.

Having decided upon skyjacking, Bob called from his home for plane reservations. He recalled great elation in that he had made "a decision on his own." He was particularly delighted to be going the next day, because there was a difficult homework assignment due which he would not have to worry about. He was very agitated and experienced sharp feelings of unreality. He took two pistols belonging to his father (he had only shot a gun once). The second gun was intended for the comrade he hoped to find in Cuba. He left home, went to New Orleans, and called his father to assure him that he was all right. Although he had left a note telling them vaguely of his plans, he was afraid they might believe he had been kidnapped. He broke his resolve and told his father that he was in New Orleans. This forced his hand. He knew his father would notify the authorities to pick him up and, therefore, he had to leave immediately. He had to make the decision in that moment either to "stand up now or to return home in defeat."

He boarded the plane and carefully questioned the stewardess about what lay under the floor, about the placement of the engines, and about the physical structure of the craft. He did not want to disable the plane if he had to shoot. En route, he asked the stewardess to be allowed to speak to the pilot. When told he could not, he got a "sick feeling inside." He leaped up, brandished both pistols, and told everyone to "stay back." At this point he admitted that he wished he were back home. He told the stewardess that he wanted to go to Cuba. He now regretted this, thinking that he should have made a more forceful statement, such as, "This plane is going to Havana." However, even after firing several shots into the floor of the craft, little notice was paid to him. (Interestingly, he wondered why he could not see bullet holes in the floor and was tempted to kneel down to see what became of them.) At one point, he put the pistol to his head, but no one paid any attention. He believed their lack of being impressed was due to his age and his acne. He eventually surrendered the guns to a male passenger and asked the crew to radio his hometown and tell his family that he was safe.

Bob readily admitted his guilt and looked back on the crime with remorse. He was studying to be a preacher for Jehovah's Witnesses; consequently, he did not drink, smoke, or curse, and frequently used Biblical quotes in his speech. His gestures were passive, his behavior circumspect.

When questioned about contrasting the crime he committed and his current piety, he replied, "Don't you see, there is no middle country for me. I must be on one side or the other of the issue of violence. If I weren't a minister, what sort of violence would I do?"

### General Comments

Encountering Bob was like finding a bird's nest on the ground. There was an obvious similarity between his and the others' family structures, and he also experienced feelings of heaviness during the waking day and of paralysis while asleep. The transcendent aspect of religious experience was again clearly manifest, as was the murderous impulse, which had been translated here into hostility against Castro. His relative failure at the development of ordinary masculine aggressive characteristics, together with other similarities that the reader will have noticed, strongly encouraged me to believe that my earlier observations had some merit.

## THE CASE OF DICK

(The following case was first brought to my attention when Dick was in the Dallas County jail charged with skyjacking. However, by the time I saw him, the charge had been reduced to illegal possession of weapons aboard an aircraft.)

Dick was a thirty-one-year-old man from the North. He was the older of two children, with a sister two years younger. His father was a service academy graduate who retired from active duty after World War II. His mother attended a prominent girl's school. The couple met when the father was thirty-eight and the mother eighteen. It was a story book romance which began at a wedding where they were both attendants.

The father's family was from Virginia and the mother's from New York. His father was the second-born in a family in which there were two sisters and five brothers. The mother was born into a family of old-line Bostonians on both sides. She had two older brothers and one older sister. She was the youngest. Her family was rigidly Roman Catholic, and her father was quite wealthy, having invented a chemical used in industrial production.

The parents' courtship had some wartime rush to it. After six months of marriage, the bride became pregnant. The second child came two years later. The father was in the Navy and may have been at sea a good part of the time. Shortly after the birth of the second child, the mother was found in bed with another man, and the father divorced her.

Custody of the patient and his sister was retained by the mother. She was well off, having been given $250,000 on the occasion of her marriage. She returned to her family home in the East, taking the children with her. The grandmother and the patient's sister each had separate bedrooms, but the patient slept with his mother until the age of nine. The mother reacted strongly to the divorce and became an alcoholic. Dick wondered if she was not a nymphomaniac, since she was remarkably promiscuous while drunk, and slept with many men. Dick was usually present in bed with them on these occasions. The mother had several additional marriages, bearing a child in one. She was pregnant at the time of this marriage. As soon as the infant was born, she left the man and the child with him. She squandered her money. She and her mother fought continuously about her promiscuity and general deportment. When she was drunk, as she often was, she made extended long-distance calls. She was belligerent and shrewish. She was unable to maintain a reasonable home, and Dick's earliest memory was of sneaking into the kitchen to make toast on Thanksgiving for his sister and himself because, in an alcoholic state, his mother had burned the dinner. His chief play object as a child was a cap gun. While living with his mother, he had no friends because the neighbors were aware of her alcoholism and kept their children away from his home.

His paternal grandmother was Episcopalian and his maternal grandparents were Irish Catholics. The mother avoided religion all week, but on Sunday she had a "vile reversion to type" with confession, Mass, and a great to-do. During these years the patient did not see his father. The latter was in South America where he had established a business. The patient, however, heard and read a great deal about his paternal uncles and grandparents who were hyper-masculine militarists. Many legends were told of them, particularly of one uncle who was a major general at the same air base where Dick was to volunteer subsequently. He felt his mother crammed Catholicism down his throat. At age seven, rejecting her hypocrisy, he began to avoid Sunday School. Later, he was reconfirmed as an Episcopalian and became rather active in that religion.

His most frequent dreams were: (1) "I have a pistol and someone else has one. I try to fire, but I am unable to do so. The other person does fire and a woman jumps into the middle. The reason I can't fire is that my hand is heavy. *Everything I do is heavy in dreams.* It is like slow motion, and I feel even in daytime I can anticipate other people's conversations," (2) "Dreams of my father doing ordinary things together," (3) "Childhood dreams all through my life of being chased all over, trying to stop someone. Such a dream never ends, and I always feel heavy, heavy. I am it [one of the two]. I am getting him or he's getting me. There is lots of upstairs or I am downstairs. Sensations of falling, like lots of times, even when I am awake, my leg twitches as if to get away from paralysis."

He termed himself never "worth a damn" at sports; possibly he was uncoordinated, and did not like them. He ran badly. He does, however, have good balance in the dark and enjoys the coordinated movements of his hands, so that when sitting in his cell he expresses his love of aircraft by moving his hands in a "piloty" fashion in which the hand is a plane, and he pretends to make approaches, take-offs, and other maneuvers. He said about this behavior, "Frequently other patients think I am crazy."

He denied sexual interest in his sister and claimed complete ignorance of these factors. He had a secret burying area in the backyard in which he accumulated objects his mother disapproved of—such as firecrackers, etc. He had an active interest in history and geography. He frequently sneaked up to the attic to read military history. At one time, he had a mongrel dog for which there was plenty of room—there were several acres of land attached to the house—but his mother and grandmother made him get rid of the dog. (At this point in the interview, he manifested more emotion than at any other, except for his later reference to his recently born son.) His most prominent collection was of letterheads he had received in reply to letters that he had written to the White House, the Senate, all the embassies, and foreign royalty, over a period of six months. He wrote such letters almost daily. According to him, at one point, a furor was created when the FBI came to his home to determine who had all these contacts. They were amazed to find an eight-year-old boy. (I am inclined to believe that this was a screen memory designed to resemble the confronting of the elders in the Temple by Jesus.)

Later, while living with his father, he was actively encouraged in his military interests. He collected guns that were heavy man-killing weapons. He had twenty of these. This collection was later sold.

When he was nine, his father came back from South America

and "saw what was going on." The patient was removed from the mother's home. He was admitted to an Episcopal school where he lived in a dormitory for two years. He claimed to have been in the upper 5 percent in grades and stated that the school was not particularly religious. He was happy there and enjoyed the association with other boys.

At age eleven he joined his father in Central America. The father was owner and operator of a prominent business. He was an important man who often drank with the important politicians, but was never too busy to help the poor. The father drank heavily, but always as a gentleman who drank well. The son was never disillusioned about his father. He stated, however, that the father may have had problems about which he did not know, since the father was married four times. He was in his fourth marriage when the boy joined them.

The patient went to both junior and senior high schools in Central America and maintained a "B" average. He was not athletically inclined. He idolized his father. When he was thirteen, his father died suddenly in bed one night. The following morning, his wife sent the patient and his sister to school without informing them what had happened. When they returned from school, they found the house filled with people, and they were then told. The patient was very angry for this concealment. He chose to manifest his idolization of his father by showing hostility toward the widow. He had pleasant memories of this family unit; he felt his father taught him everything a man should know, such as all about "syph, clap, prostitutes." When he was twelve, his father bought him his first whore.

When he expressed hostility after his father's death, the widow kicked him out of the house and he lived on the veranda, wrapping himself at night in rags. At one time, having no shoes, he stole a pair from a locker room. He was caught and had to face his first charge of petty larceny. At this point in the interview he was obliged to remind me that his father was a big man whose death had produced headlines.

When he was fourteen, an Episcopal priest learned of the situation and arranged to send him to a boy's home in the States. He lived there until he was seventeen. His relationship with the professors was good. He made good grades and really "dug" the girls. He was quite active riding horses with girls in the neighborhood. According to him, this often ended up in haystacks, since the girls in the school were curious about this boy who was the first from the home to attend the local high school. It was not clear from the interview whether he graduated from high school. At seventeen, he left the home and volunteered in the Army with the intention of becoming an airborne trooper in the same branch as his uncle, the major general. The general advised him that enlistment was not the way to become a general, in spite of which he enlisted and was sent to Colorado. He claimed that because they knew about his uncle, he became a scapegoat. "They rode my ass to get rid of their underlying failures." He was, he felt, a good soldier who kept his things well and scored high in company activity.

Once he was AWOL for four hours because of a simple delay. Upon return to camp, no issue was made of it by the sergeant, but Dick went to his quarters, got a pistol, went out on the parade grounds, and deliberately shot himself in the abdomen, aiming at his kidney. (He had only one kidney because of a horseshoe defect which was detected and corrected at age eleven.) This wound tore things up internally quite badly, and he was severed from the Army at age eighteen.

Following this, he returned to his mother's home. In the next three months, he drove all over and had no recollection of where he was during that time. Subsequently, he appeared in Houston and re-enlisted in the Army under the same name but with a different number. It was soon learned that he had had prior enlistment, and he was again severed as being "undesirable." In the latter part of 1957, he was in an Army hospital and claimed that he did not see, but was very much stimulated by the news of Sputnik I.

He returned to his mother, but within three days he was fully tired of her. He packed his Army fatigues, his combat boots, and a heavy revolver. He bought a two-way ticket to Havana (which was required) and went there to fight for Castro. At the Jose Marti airport, the customs officials found this strange collection and apparently, passed him right on in because "they must have been Castro sympathizers." At that time he had no notion that Castro would later appear to be a Communist. His only interest was that there was a war in Cuba and that he could get into it. At this point, showing excitement, he stated, "You must understand how desperately I felt about being a military man and the completeness of my sense of failure following my second discharge." From Havana he bussed to Santiago and took to the hills, walking for hours to establish contact with the Castro forces. He claimed to have taken part in harassing activities as a part of these forces, but did not believe that he was a party to any killings, since harassment was the aim. He was captured by elements of the Cuban First Army. He was later deported from a Havana prison through the actions of the U.S. Consulate and returned to Miami. He felt his real trouble began then.

Immediately following his return from Cuba, he left Miami for California in order to visit an Army nurse who had cared for him during his last hospitalization. On the way, in Arizona, he picked up two hitchhikers and, feeling a wild sense of abandon, he decided to create his own revolution here. They went on a spree of armed robberies between Colorado and Illinois in which they robbed small loan companies and service stations, using unloaded pistols. He was arrested in Baltimore and was sent to Spring Grove Hospital with the diagnosis of schizophrenic reaction, paranoid type, with delusions of grandeur. He was in treatment until December, 1959.

Upon discharge, he went to New York and got a job with Pan American Airlines. During this period, he was dating a girl whose father was an Annapolis graduate. He impregnated her, and they married in July, 1960. She miscarried in August, and they were divorced in September. Shortly thereafter, his past criminal record came to the attention of his employers and he was discharged.

He returned to Miami and was employed by the Lineas Chilea Airlines as General Operations Manager. It was a small outfit which managed two flights a day. Pay was not high. He met, dated, and married a German girl whose father had been Chief of Staff under General Kesselring. He maintained an extensive correspondence with his father-in-law, being particularly interested in "what the U.S. bombing pressure was like for the troops exposed to it." Since the airline did not pay well, he and this wife went to California. They arrived there with thirty-three dollars. He hocked his watch for twenty dollars. He got a job as an apartment house manager and then as an insurance adjuster. He then began buying inexpensive cigarette vending machines. When he and his wife left California a year later, he sold out the vending business for $12,000. This move was partly dictated by the impending birth of a child.

They moved to Maryland, rented a house, and had a baby girl. Then, he rented a 40-foot boat in Maryland and failed to return it. Sometime later, he was arrested in Boston. He was transferred to the state hospital, at which point he achieved release through a writ of *habeas corpus.*

During his stay in the hospital, the wife became involved with another man and showed little interest in him. Again he returned to Miami and flew to Puerto Rico, looking for a job in the airline industry, but had no luck. He returned to Miami and went on to Houston where he got a job with General Electric and became financially solvent, so that he soon had an apartment filled with furniture and a home ready for his wife. The day before her arrival, he called her and she said, "I don't know, maybe I won't come." Greatly angered by this response, he exploded in acute rage and said, "To hell with it." He rented a car and began to drive. He drove from Houston to Los Angles to Colorado and back to Houston. *He repeated this loop three times in as many weeks,* ending up in Tucumcari, New Mexico. He did not know what became of the rented car, but at this point he bought an automobile closely resembling that of the New Mexico State highway patrol and obtained a uniform of the same type. He staked himself out in the middle of the desert, chased down motorists, and gave them tickets. He would then permit them to bribe him to tear up the ticket. After three months of this, he was arrested and thrown in jail for ninety days. Life there was a horrifying experience for him.

During this incarceration, he received letters from his mother saying, "Come home, come home," and that she had a job with a large lumber company waiting for him. He returned home, took the job, and felt that his performance at work was good. He was always able to get extremely good letters of recommendation wherever he had worked. But he began to become increasingly angry with his mother, blew up, quit his job, and went to Canada. There he was arrested for speeding and placed in a government hospital, then deported through psychiatric repatriation to a hospital in the Miami area. During this time, he was extremely paranoid and believed the hospital to be a government trap. When bored in the hospital, he became involved in discussions which, he claimed, were simply "for fun. . . ." He and two other patients discussed the possibility of kidnapping the Kennedy children. Another patient overheard these conversations and reported them. Consequently, he is now and will remain in the future on the Secret Service roster. When he is released from any facility, the Secret Service is notified to resume surveillance. In any event, when released from the hospital, he promptly wrote a large number of hot checks in Miami and immediately left for Canada, where he made tentative efforts to become a mercenary in Biafra.

While in Canada, he precipitously married a Canadian girl. The marriage was just as precipitously annulled. While there, he experienced acute feelings that his life was catching up with him. He was particularly disturbed about a number of worthless checks he had written in Houston which exposed him to criminal charges there. So he flew from Canada to Austin, Texas, and committed himself in the Austin State Hospital, presumably to invalidate any legal charges in Texas. While there, he was offended by the facilities in which he was detained. He jimmied a window and, using the age-old device of sheets tied together, let himself to the ground and went again to Miami. He again turned himself in, this time to the Florida State Hospital, and was placed in maximum security. Once again, he was apparently trying to establish himself as a psychotic in order to invalidate any charges that might be brought against him in Florida for having written worthless checks. After a stay of some time, he claims to have bought a key from an attendant and to have let himself out of the hospital.

He rented a car and drove to Los Angeles. He got himself another apartment and another job. Also, he got married. Feeling the pressure of things catching up with him again, he flew to upstate New York, crossed over the border and robbed a branch of the Royal Bank of Canada. He was again put into a Canadian hospital. He left that hospital to be transferred to a psychiatric hospital in Los Angeles. When, after some time, the court-appointed psychiatrist failed to call him for an interview, he had himself released on bond, which he immediately jumped.

He then went to Maryland and started a K-9 dog business during the riots. He was extremely proud of this company and of his record in it. He protected the stores of Jewish merchants in the Negro ghettos and claimed that those for whom he was responsible suffered no losses. He was also very proud that he had had the responsibility for several million dollars in merchandise and that he had been completely honest about it. He had organized his company like a military outfit with himself as captain, and lieutenants, sergeants, corporals, and dogs under him. He stated that within ninety days he was grossing $8,000 per month leasing his dogs. He said that he had become a real expert in the care of German shepherds, about which he is very sentimental.

During this time, he was, of course, dealing with heads of police departments, even though a wanted poster with his photograph on it was distributed all over the country. His wife became pregnant and *he knew he would be caught*. Accordingly, even though he was at the moment happy and respected, owned sixteen acres of land on the outskirts of town, and had good credit, he sold his business to an associate for only $1,200, which he considered to be "running money." He and his wife fled to San Francisco to hide. They had been told to expect the baby on March 13 (his father's birthday), but she developed a slow amniotic leak on January 9. They again sold everything they possessed for cash, in order to run, and he put her on a plane for Los Angeles to be with her people at the time of delivery. She arrived safely and a baby boy was born on January 10. He bought a car and drove to Los Angeles with the intention of seeing his child. When he telephoned his wife to say that he was coming out, she informed him that the FBI had a stake-out waiting for him. Unable to see his son, he drove to Shreveport without sleep. He had about $5,000 in cash, of which he wired $1,750 to his wife, while he was staying at a Holiday Inn there.

He chartered a twin engine plane in Shreveport, saying that he was going to Memphis. He intended to skyjack the plane to go to Cuba. The pilot, however, was a young fellow who, like himself, had a wife and a newborn son. He was unable to carry through with his plan. He then decided to take a 727 out of Memphis, still intending to skyjack. When the plane took off, he was deeply engrossed in thoughts about his father, uncle, and son. He weighed their value over against the concept of being a turncoat, and was finally unable to pull his pistol because he felt obliged to "pass on" a patriotic tradition to his child.

When he arrived in Philadelphia, he concluded that he could at least get out of the country by going to Mexico and immediately boarded a plane for Mexico City. When it landed in Dallas, an FBI agent came aboard and arrested him. The final charge was not that of skyjacking but of possession of arms aboard an aircraft. At the time of his arrest, he estimated that he had traveled well over 200,000 miles in a ten-year period.

At the point in the interview when he referred to the Kennedy children, he suddenly asked in an intense fashion, "Am I a sociopath?" When I inquired what he meant, he said that if he felt that during the remainder of his life he would continue to hurt other people as he had been doing, he would "hang it up," and he gestured with his hands to indicate a rope around his neck. He went on to add, however, that he believed that he had passed through a "crisis" between Nashville and Philadelphia when he had made the choice between skyjacking and escaping.

## General Comments

The reader will appreciate the intensity of my excitement at the realization of the similarities of this case to the rest of the sample, and the dissimilarities. In spite of the wildly improbable aura of certain events, enough of the specifics have been confirmed by out-side sources to make it possible to assume that it is a basically honest record.

What intrigued me particularly about the actions of the first three cases was that they had seen their fathers as the epitome of violence when they were children and rejcted that image. Now, however, their acts seemed to be almost a carbon copy of those of the individual whom they had denied. Dick, however, did not have the same hostile anti-father image. He rebelled against the maternal image and against religious thinking. He participated in a variety of criminal activities which were often impulsive and highly dangerous. Many of the wild endeavors which he actually carried out would have fitted the wishful fantasies of the rest of the group in their more desperate moments. Yet, in the final analysis, he could not act because of his respect for the *Patria,* as expressed both by the male figures of his family, as well as by the concept of fatherland.

The tedious details of Dick's tendency to travel have been care-fully preserved in this report because of its importance in connec-tion with a similar tendency in later cases. At another point, all of these will be seen to be related to the only article I was able to find in medical literature with some direct bearing on skyjacking. (See Chapter V.)

Insight is not a miraculous thing. It is preceded by hours and years of just such tedium before one finds it possible to look beyond the simple content of interviews. Without twenty years of patient interviewing, it would have been quite impossible for me to have heard the communication of these patients.

In point of fact, the significant theoretical concepts were not even new to me. I had been playing with most of them for several years, in a volume of short stories,[1] without even being aware of that fact. It was only when I read the galley proofs recently that the clear connection came through.

[1] David G. Hubbard, *Some Skunks and Other Cases* (Dallas: Genesis Press, 1971).

# V

# Gravity as a Psychiatric Construct

At this point in the study, it occurred to me that I had been automatically presuming that the effects of gravity on personality constituted a recognized subject of study in psychiatry and had been treated as such by others in the field. I was unable, however, to recall anything specific, which prompted me to undertake a systematic search of the psychiatric literature. It turned out that my search yielded no direct references to gravity at all, and little interest even in the physical organs through which man becomes aware of the force of gravity. When Freud dealt with dreams of falling and flying, he assigned them to everyday psychopathology, and seemed unaware of the fact that such dreams recurred intensely over extended periods in many individuals. He regarded such dreams largely as recollections of childhood play with adults, in which the subject was raised and lowered. Yet, Freud noted: *"I can not, however, disguise from myself that I am unable to produce any complete explanation of this class of typical dreams."* [1] On the other hand, he related the symptom of daytime "falling," exhibited in certain neurotic conditions, to guilt—to attacks by the superego.

Ferenczi described transference phenomena displayed by certain patients who experienced giddiness on rising from the psycho-

---

[1] S. Freud, *The Interpretation of Dreams* (London: Hogarth Press, 1953), pp. 271–276. These and the following quotations are from Vols. IV and V of this edition.

analytic couch.[2] He held that such patients were deriving a sense of well-being from the transference situation and, when this state was suddenly shattered by the termination of the hour, it was as if they "had fallen from the clouds." Earlier in his *Thalassa*,[3] Ferenczi had tried to interest Freud again in the subject of "cosmic feeling," "oceanic feeling," and in dreams of flight and falling. Unfortunately, his effort was misspent, for Freud failed to acknowledge *Thalassa* and its contribution.

Schilder noted the implication of the vestibular apparatus in certain mental disturbances:

> The vestibular nerve occupies a special position among the senses. Its sensations do not form a part of our conscious knowledge of the world. The vestibular apparatus is not only an organ for perception [of movements and gravity], it is an organ which gives rise to very important reflexes, to turning and progressive movement, [and] which influence the muscle tone of the body. It is in this way a great system for orienting ourselves in the world. This system is, of course, not isolated but cooperates with the other systems of orientation, especially that of the optic perceptions. It is more closely related to a primitive motility than is vision. Whenever we perceive an object, we have already the basic knowledge about our body and about the attitude of our body. The perceiving individual gets a knowledge of an object and the object, as such, provokes immediately attitudes in him. These attitudes make a fuller perception possible. We would expect that such a sensory organ, with only half conscious impressions and leading to a motility of an instinctive and primitive type, would be very sensitive to emotions and would therefore play an important part in neuroses and psychoses. Organic changes in the vestibular apparatus will be reflected in the psychic structure. They will not only influence the tone, the vegetative system, and the attitudes of the body, but they must also change our whole perceptive apparatus and even our consciousness. These general considerations

---

[2] S. Ferenczi, *Sensations of Giddiness at the End of the Psychoanalytic Session, Further Contributions to the Theory and Technique of Psychoanalysis* (London: Hogarth Press, 1950), pp. 239-241.

[3] S. Ferenczi, *Thalassa, PSQ Quarterly* (1938). German original (1924).

make it possible that the study of the vestibular apparatus may have great importance for the understanding of psychotic and neurotic states.[4]

I found no further rewards in the psychiatric literature. If the heretical nature of my thinking was confirmed by that discovery, such heresy was nevertheless compensated for by the possibility that struggling through uncharted territory might result in valuable new maps. Consequently, I redirected my attention to the data yielded by the first four skyjackers, while waiting for opportunities to increase my sample.

The capacity to stand and walk is innate, not taught. As quickly as our neurological development allows it, we are bound and determined to stand erect, a physical ability unique to man alone— the erect posture. Was it only chance that in each of the four cases the skyjacker *always* used some form of the verb "to stand," in describing the crime? Why was body image *always* involved in their attempts to give an account of themselves in relation to the event? These men had been driven to stand on their own two feet, to face the "mysteries," and to go from this planet to a more pleasing place.

One must never forget that skyjackings take place *in the air* and involve *vertical* movement. It is also important to remember that these men managed to *communicate* some part of themselves during the interviews and gained a certain empathy from us. The empathy, I believe, emerged from the early wish to be completely free from the force of gravity and to be able to fly like birds—a wish we all share. Their attempts "to stand up," and "to face the powers that be," expressed not an element of "manhood" but of "personhood."

Watching adult psychiatric patients approach new or strange situations and older, badly managed ones, I have wished repeatedly over the years that I could instill in them once again that willingness and daring of their childhood that impelled them to "get off their knees and walk like men." They possessed that courage in child-

---

[4] P. Schilder, "The Vestibular Apparatus in Neurosis and Psychosis," *Journal of Nervous and Mental Diseases*, 78 (1933), 1–23.

hood, no matter how timorous and neurotic they became later in life. I have wished they could feel the same enthusiastic willingness to *attempt* to be a human being once again, and to stand erect in the face of the odds and the possibility of failure.

The literature of the body image implies, for the most part, that the human being's body image is vertical, but it is not very precise on the subject. Schilder, for one, fails to attach the body image to the ground; it is generally taken for granted. But in taking it for granted, we leave ourselves unaware of opportunities to observe meanings whenever we move our own body image verbally, and whenever we move the body image of others verbally, in order to express complex, *non-verbal* feelings through "the emotion of the motion." [5] That is, we employ linguistic gymnastics to convey our meaning.

Also I must stress the frequency with which both body movement and body image were used by these men during the interviews. Often the men would adopt physical postures to illustrate what they had to say. Just as often they employed body *images* in attempting to convey sensations and thought processes. Schilder[6] emphasized again and again that body image tends toward entropy and has to receive sustained and continuous inputs if it is to continue to exist. In this connection, one immediately recalls the startling, common tendency in these men to walk vigorously or ride great distances— activities that produced a physical stimulus of the equilibratory apparatus. I got the distinct impression from their accounts that they would begin to "fade" from their own awareness from one moment to the next, and that physical movement had the capacity to reconstruct their body images for them.

I have often noticed that prisoners whose physical movement is restricted suffer loss of body image. Unless they find some way to move about, their body image will "thin out." The healthiest prisoners I have seen take regular daily walks in prison yards and trot around a track.

[5] Herbert Haynes, M.D., has suggested the use of this term. It is very apt.
[6] P. Schilder, *The Image and Appearance of the Human Body* (New York: International Universities Press, 1950), p. 183.

If the struggle against gravity is indeed inherent in man, then his history and behavior ought to reflect it.

At the moment of birth, the force of gravity is the first thing the infant becomes aware of when he is thrust out of the sac of amniotic fluid in which he had been suspended.[7] In studies of newborn infants it has been noted that the only fear common to all is the fear of falling—*an expression of their increased awareness of the strange new force of gravity.* The fear of gravitational pull may well serve as the paradigm of all subsequent fears. Certainly the attempt to overcome gravity constitutes the principal struggle of the early years of existence. The child must first manage to control his position in the crib, and then to sit, crawl, walk, run, and jump. Gravity is the cause of the first ego strain. One may say, "Where id was, there shall ego be," [8] *and its perpetual antagonist is gravity, which speaks through its own organ.*

The importance of the development and integrity of body image has been stressed by Gesell.[9] He concluded that pre-natal human development related to these factors is primary and basic. He discerned five areas of interweaving patterns: (1) patterns in the autonomic or vaso-vegetative areas of homeostasis; (2) patterns of sleeping and waking and states of consciousness; (3) patterns of respiration which also anticipate speech, language, and ideation; (4) patterns of tone in response to global perception, especially of gravity with the evolution and development of the vestibular system, from which perception of time, space, reality, and object relationships evolve; (5) patterns of motor activity arising from the tonic neck-righting responses, and from which cortical dominance patterns may also rise.

Gesell further indicated that these functional patterns are the

[7] An environment comparable to amniotic suspension is employed to study relative weightlessness and the effect of sensory deprivation.

[8] S. Freud, *New Introductory Lectures on Psychoanalysis* in *The Standard Edition of the Complete Psychological Works of Sigmund Freud,* Vol. 22, 1932–1936 (London: Hogarth Press, 1964), p. 80.

[9] A. Gesell, *The Embryology of Behavior—The Beginning of the Human Mind* (New York: Harper Bros., 1945).

biological basis or embryology of all subsequent human behavior.

Bender concluded that the plasticity she observed in schizophrenic chidren is a primary embryologic feature that accounts for lagging and regressive, as well as accelerating, patterns of maturation.[10] She saw in the schizophrenic infant a continual failure to balance, to integrate, and to pattern primary functions under homeostatic control.[11]

If, as I propose, the force of gravity is the fundamental unit of continuous, comprehensible reality, it ought not to be surprising that children characteristically dream about flying, with or without wings, as the ultimate of free self-expression, and that they resort to flying dreams when they feel tied down. So I had to ask myself why these four men did not relate flying dreams. Was it because the interview was inadequate? Were their religious feelings compensating them sufficiently to balance out the need for their feelings to emerge in dreams? Dick was the only one who came close to having flying dreams. By his own admission, he spent hours at a time using his hands in imitation of flight. And he was the only one who rejected religion at an early age and frequently engaged in criminal activity. Athough I felt certain that flying dreams were to have a prominent place in the "syndrome," at this juncture I had to place my trust in the cases that would eventually accumulate.

At about this point in the study, I found the only reference in psychiatric literature that seemed to bear directly on the cases at hand. Miller and Zarcone reported the results of interviews with forty-nine severely disturbed individuals who had been detained by airport authorities for seventy-two hours for psychiatric examination.[12] They found that these individuals were generally psychotics, with paranoia, anxiety, and euphoria evidenced as a syndrome. They concluded that *those manifesting the syndrome were*

[10] Lauretta Bender, "The Concept of Plasticity in Childhood Schizophrenia," in *Psychopathology of Schizophrenics,* ed. Hoch and Zubin (New York: Grune & Stratton, 1950).

[11] When we met to go over my data, her first comment about the whole survey was, "Why, those are my schizophrenic babies, thirty years later."

[12] Warren B. Miller and Vincent Zarcone, "Psychiatric Behavior Disorders at an International Airport," *Archives of Environmental Health,* 17 (Sept. 1968).

*peregrinating paranoids who used the airlines to create interpersonal distance, to achieve immediate closeness, to vary the environment, and to act out delusional systems on a grand scale.*[13] The incidence of this severe disturbance was found to be one per million passengers. Additionally, they noted that individuals who were picked up for psychiatric examination at airports were almost entirely of this type, whereas patients from the general population who were subjected to seventy-two hours of similar examination were mostly depressed, alcoholic, and consciously suicidal individuals. On the basis of these comparative results, they concluded that airports appeared to have such features *as tended to attract those with a specific psychiatric profile.*

At this time, I acquired four more cases for study, each of whom was to present a host of new variables.

It must be kept in mind, while reading the case histories, that personality traits had to be isolated in the course of a single interview in most instances. Still, the interviews were from two to six hours in duration, with such added advantage as comes from the use of this type of interview. Even so, in typewritten form, each interview yielded from twenty-five to sixty pages of material, and it would be presumptuous of me to assume that so limited an account could convey the complexities of any given human life. We are all, of course infinitely more complicated and even after hundreds of hours with a patient, many surprises pop up to confound the psychiatrist. There was, nevertheless, something remarkable about this group of interviews. Both generally and specifically, there were factors that can only be characterized as unique.

Above all, in over twenty years of psychiatric practice, I would not have thought it possible that a group of relatively small size, drawn on the basis of a common endeavor of any sort, was capable of yielding so many pronouncedly common personality traits or so distinctly common a psychopathologic profile.

---

[13] Each of the factors listed closely fits Dick in particular, but Brian and Elmer as well. As will be observed again and again, they will play a part in many other cases. Their tendency towards lateral movement is too striking to be overlooked.

# VI

# A Quartet of Patients

## THE CASE OF MARK [1]

Mark was a young man of mixed foreign ancestry, serving a sentence for attempted skyjacking which occurred in 1965. The interview was hampered by his rudimentary knowledge of English.

The patient had three older brothers and two younger sisters. The father was a fisherman when he worked, which he did infrequently, and he had served two terms in prison. He drank and was quite violent. He completely subjugated his wife. Mark felt that he was beaten more often than his siblings and distinctly recalled that his father once attempted to kill him and he was rescued by his mother.

The mother was a religious zealot, a compulsive churchgoer. She constantly reminded her children of God's power to save them and worried about their salvation because of her fear of the evil influence of their father. The patient closely identified with the maternal side of the family, but he claimed never to have been interested in religion. "Inside me, I was closest to my sisters," he said.

He displayed behavior problems in school and was often truant. He completed only the ninth grade.

He reported that sexual experiences began at age thirteen. He married at age sixteen and divorced a year later. The marriage was stormy and unstable from the beginning. The divorce was brought on by Mark's alcoholism and his wife's infidelity. The patient be-

[1] Interviewed by Dr. Don Johnston at a time when we were still unsure of our specifics. Later he became essential to the creation of control series and other matters.

lieved that his uncle had stolen his wife and searched for him with the intention of murdering him.

From age fifteen, Mark spent most of his time in prison. There, too, he manifested behavior problems and on one occasion he spent thirteen months in solitary confinement.

The year 1965 found him serving a sentence for a series of burglaries. He managed to escape from the reformatory, which was located on a small, nearby deserted island. First, he broke into an empty house and stole food and a shotgun with ammunition. Then, he went to the airport, which handled inter-island tourist flights as well as private aircraft. He hoped to board a plane by threatening to kill the airport officials. He broke into the control tower and held its operators at gunpoint while waiting for a plane to land, but an official managed to contact and warn an approaching plane. Soon afterward, the police forced him to surrender after a gun battle.

He disclaimed any intention of suicide. He harbored no dislike for the airlines or for the United States, and had no thought of going to Cuba. He explained that the attempt was a matter of expediency, because it was the quickest way to escape capture.

He smoked throughout the interview and cursed frequently, but did not seem to be either elated or depressed.

## General Comments

This case did little more than show up the consistent nature of previously noted family constellation. Here again were the violent father, zealot mother, big brothers, little sisters, rejection of mother's religious ideals, truancy, criminal activity, and the "do or die" aspect of the final stand. No information was gathered relating to body image.

Of new interest is the fact that Mark had a low tolerance for alcohol and began to drink heavily at an unusually early age. This symptom was to recur in subsequent cases. Most did not drink. Those who did so had sharp difficulty with physical and emotional instability.

## THE CASE OF OSCAR

The patient was white, twenty-six years old. His family consisted of mother, father, and eight children. Oscar was the sixth, but the fifth, a boy, had died in infancy. There survived four boys and three girls: In sequence, the first two were twin boys, then a girl, another girl, the patient, another girl, and a boy. As a result of the death of the fifth-born, there was an eight-year gap between the fourth-born and the patient, and only three and a half years between him and the seventh-born.

Every one of Oscar's siblings appeared to lead uneventfully normal lives; all but the youngest were married and settled.

The patient's father, when young, had been deserted by his father; in turn, he too deserted his own family. He had been in prison for a minor theft. In Oscar's words, "In my opinion, he was a psychopath as he was very violent." The beatings he inflicted were sudden and intensely furious, and often they were directed against his wife and daughters, as well as against an occasional drunk. He had no physical conflicts with policemen or sober men of his own size. Apparently he did not need alcohol to mobilize his violence.

The mother experienced serious early deprivation, for her mother died when she was two and her father when she was eleven. She was extremely neglected in childhood. She was addicted to candy and put inordinate emphasis on food. During her teens, two of her brothers drowned on the same day, one trying to save the other. According to the patient, the mother did not appear to be emotionally bigoted or zealously religious. (It might be noted that the patient himself espoused marked agnosticism.) In his view, his mother was, "Always busy working for someone, raising kids, and raising her own family," and was characterized by rectitude, hard work, and devotion to the Protestant ethic.

Oscar's earliest recollection was traced to the period before he had learned to walk. He remembered himself on a blanket on the living room floor, "unable to rise."

When Oscar was seven, his father deserted the family. Soon after, they were living in squalor in a slum area. There was a lot of violence in the neighborhood and he was instructed by his mother to protect his little sister.

He recollected many incidents of violence, bullying, terror, and being at the mercy of bigger and more violent boys. His dreams during this period centered on being naked in school, or running from a monster, only to find himself paralyzed and unable to escape. He "froze up and couldn't get away." In another recurring dream, "my bed was full of scorpions. I've been on my feet. It was like having the D.T.'s. It was like a sea or swarm of scorpions on the floor. I don't know if it was a dream or a hallucination." While describing the dreams, he chuckled. The dreams of paralysis extended well into his teens, and the dream of scorpions up to the present.

He was hesitant to admit having been a loner through his school years. Only occasionally did he associate with his peers, and then only in destructive antics. "We tried to derail a steam locomotive once, put it over on the tracks, and push it off. We had a gang war with some other characters down the way, hailing stones at one another." (Chuckle.)

Oscar exhibited a pronounced tendency to restrict the information he was willing to share. He absolutely refused to offer any data about his relationship with his younger sister between his seventh and twelfth years. "The information is priviliged and I'd rather just leave that door closed."

When he was thirteen, a friend told him about the purpose of genitals. In referring to masturbation, he said, "I *stumbled* onto it when I was fourteen." From then until he was nineteen, he was "almost a maniac for sex." At the age of nineteen, he went to a prostitute and discovered that "a vagina was simply a canal, a point of conception, and no seventh heaven as others had told me." After that experience, his sexual activity was extremely restricted, averaging one intercourse a year, all with prostitutes.

In high school, he had less than a dozen dates altogether, "Oh, I could ask for dates, but the girl usually made the first move. All my life I've raved. I was ostracized, and I had a low social standing in my hometown." He emphasized repeatedly that one with his social standing would be most *ill-advised to ask for dates*.

In high school, he developed an interest in aviation and joined a school society of radio hams and student pilots. In aviation he learned slowly. His attention wandered. He would gaze at the ground and forget classroom instructions. He achieved a very limited proficiency, with less than thirteen hours of dual flight instruction, barely enough to solo. (I do not believe he ever flew solo.) His coordination was extremely poor. In steering into a turn, he would lean away from the bank rather than into it. He was never able to incorporate the aircraft into his body image.

He was fourteen at the time of Sputnik I, and was swept up into the rocket craze of the time. He related, "I was playing with a little aluminum cylinder stuffed with black powder, and I was trying to light it with a match." (Chuckles.) His mother disciplined him with a piece of rope. He recalled the subsequent series of space activities with a surprising accuracy and had much sympathy for the Russian dog, Laika. He refused to say which of the astronauts he identified with most or wanted to have as a friend or father. He was asked and he refused three times. He watched television often, and always followed the space events. He was strongly stimulated by Apollo 8 and showed keen interest in Mars, which he described as "a weird-looking thing, an alien world, a virgin untouched. There's no telling what they may find there." He would very much like to be either an astronaut or a commercial pilot, but feels that both goals are beyond him.

He was involved in ROTC during his junior year. Fantasies of rank, power, and destruction were significant themes, and he also became interested in dynamite. "I was actually living under a brainwashed condition. I was a National Guardsman and I was in an operational company. I hadn't been to basic, and many of them had experience over me, and I was weak, thick, and slow. They were pushing me in because I actually was effectively a moron. They thought I was lazy too. They were shouting at me and I was being teased by many people."

In his nineteenth year, he experienced an acute psychotic episode in summer ROTC camp, which terminated in a suicide attempt. "I was looking at the future, I had few friends, and I also had a poor reputation. I was ashamed of myself. I was nineteen and old enough to be living on my own and I was living off my own brother." He was placed in the state mental hospital. He felt that drugs were used on him, that people were "playing with my brain golgi cells. When such a cell is stimulated, it is like a miniature tape recorder from which one can derive a song that they can't remember, even word for word." He believed that as the result of this manipulation, "people have just become unhinged, their inner structure has just collapsed, that people are teased to absolute insanity."

It was a particularly interesting notion of Oscar's on the subject of his breakdown that a "time capsule" inside had been dissolved by waters or acids, with the resultant loss of structure and identity.

Of the eight years that followed his first hospital admission, he spent five in custodial care. He held minor, temporary jobs between his periods in hospital. He did not date. He often developed strong fixations on good-looking girls, but never spoke to them. He became involved only if they approached him, and these contacts were extremely limited. He described himself as "rundown, not mentally efficient, not mentally strong," and found it impossible "to be at a job, much less to do a good one."

He felt he would "as soon be awake as asleep because I had nightmares." These frequently consisted of his blanket's falling from his bed to the floor and becoming covered with scorpions, and of his having a "fit" at the thought of retrieving it because of the danger of the scorpions. He described them as being "murderous, striking without warning, and really for no reason."

Between two early hospital stays, he drank too much and was arrested once. He found that drinking did not help relieve his terror. He was dependent upon his family and embarrassed in his relationships with peers. He felt he was "strange."

His hospital records were available to student nurses. Oscar intensely resented this fact; also, he believed that drugs were used on him and that he was being given a "life tease, from the cradle to the grave." He felt they were "taking my mind," that it was "a brain attack," and that it was of intensely long duration. "My mood is usually below par." He frequently experienced the feeling that someone was forcing entry into his home, and he heard voices. It was difficult for him to distinguish between the voice he claimed as his own and those he claimed were voices about him. When he raved, he spoke about "flighting, aviation, the army, and mental hospitals. I often spoke about space." He also used the phrase "it's fantastic," and pointed out that this was a famous old Buck Rogers saying.

It seems that both his auditory hallucinations and his recollections of talking to himself revolved most frequently around his anger, in which he "boiled over with fury about the problems involved in hospitalization, particularly having student nurses know about me."

When Oscar was not in the hospital, he was subject to frequent fits of violent behavior. He would throw stones at people and beat them. They were usually neighbors who were teasing him, he felt. He also cursed at them, because "my brain was being milked."

He felt he was being bullied and believed that "people are hairless apes. They're ruled by their emotions. They're also stupid and dominant, also very cold." He felt that "if one is not very careful, he may become involved with people and they're very poor, and it's a poor idea." It was his desire to be a commercial pilot. He spoke with some excitement of aircraft "orbiting the field."

His skyjacking attempt followed his discharge from the hospital in the fall of 1968. He had been receiving an allowance of five dollars a week from his mother, which he saved toward an attempt to escape from home. With the aid of part-time employment, he accumulated a total of two hundred dollars. He asked for and received a visa application to Cuba, but never completed or submitted it. He made no effort to obtain a passport because he believed that a psychotic could not receive one. He was convinced that psychotics were regarded as criminals or convicts and passports were consequently denied to them. He lived in hatred of the state hospital, although he had been discharged from it. He did not think of skyjacking an aircraft until the day before attempting it. The idea followed an event which he described in these words: "Well, somebody got on my rear and pushed it clear through and teased me even harder." Whether homosexual rape had actually taken place or it had been delusional could not be established. The following day, he bought a revolver—the first firearm he had ever owned.

Oscar believed he could find sanctuary in Cuba, because "it's a foreign government." He felt he could apply for sanctuary there and request that the government guard him against "the voices," whereas, in England, for example, "the voices would undoubtedly set in as soon as the plane made its approach to land." He thought that when he petitioned the Cuban government for sanctuary, the event "would have been publicized. There would have been a public reaction." He followed this by saying, "I actually wanted to use a submachine gun on my hometown [chuckle]." Another fantasy he had in this area was, "I was going to come back. I was going to land in a Russian helicopter and start shooting up the state hospital and the legislature."

Following a different track, he said, "All I wanted to do was get away and I'm not very physically strong. I want to be a private person and not be picked on nor molested by homosexuals." Then he reverted to the track of his homicidal wish toward his hometown and again broke into chuckles.

He saw no reason why he would not reach Cuba, since he had been impressed by the ease with which others had accomplished it, with objects like "a shoe box and even a switchblade. I thought all I had to do was bluff my way through." He was apparently struck by the fact that people talked about skyjackers, that they attracted a great deal of attention.

He flew from his hometown to a city 800 miles away. There he changed planes and proceeded with his loosely planned skyjacking. He went to the restroom and got the revolver out of his belt. He accosted the stewardess, pointed the gun at her, and said, "Havana, go to Havana." She did not argue. Oscar had planned to bluff his way and he was experiencing paralysis at the thought of pulling the trigger if she did not comply. The pilot said he had to refuel in New Orleans and made no effort to grab the gun. ("He could have, easily.") Oscar described himself as being "in a corner" that he kept backing into. "They gained more confidence all along. I knew I was screwed. It was all over." He said he knew the pilot was lying about the range of the aircraft, but he felt he was more or less at "their" mercy because they had the capacity "to ignore me, move past me, and go about their functions, just looking at me." When the plane landed in New Orleans, Oscar moved back to the galley. At this juncture, he had the impression that someone came out of a mirror. He said, "The mirror opened and some kind of a guy just popped out." This was an FBI agent who happened to be a passenger and was the last person to leave the airplane. Oscar said that the agent teased and mocked him until he got the gun. Just before he surrendered it, after making many threats, he fired one shot into the floor. At that point, the FBI agent grabbed the gun and Oscar became acutely fearful for his life, expecting to be shot. He screamed and was terribly frightened. During the interview, he said, with a great deal of contempt and anger, that the FBI agent had boasted about his own bravery and that he did not think the agent was really entitled to do so.

Oscar felt that he was incapable of murder or rape, that he would simply freeze if he attempted either. At the same time, he anticipated death at the hands of others and the idea of suicide was not intolerable to him.

In the same vein, he was intensely fearful in prison. He feared he would be ripped with a razor blade, or raped, or killed. He expected to die in jail, probably at the hands of a homosexual or someone violent. He wished he had alcohol, because it "helps to pass the time, even though it doesn't make me really happy, but it helps diminish the feeling that someone is doing something behind my back." He was essentially resigned to his death, although he felt "I'm just going to break. I'm going to be a complete dolt. They're going to tear me to bits. I'm going to scream and bawl. They're just going to laugh and make it worse." He also said, "That's right. They're horrible. They cross-train you. They get an impression across. Then after you react, they go against it or punish it, and they get you completely confused. They actually want to commit perversions on you and physical violence, unheard-of physical violence. They want to push eyes out, they want to lacerate and mutilate and bludgeon. They're horrible. I despise these people." During his hospitalization, he frequently dreamed about deaths in his family or about being punished for a crime. The dreams were extremely real and he would wake up screaming. Often, they were associated with sleepwalking.

Oscar stated that all he wanted was a normal life, to be unmolested, his mind unentered, and no perversions performed upon him. He believed that the brain is a storage battery which transmits electricity when one speaks, and that there is a transistor device under one's skull. When he was urged to be more precise, he said that the device might well be located in his ears where he experienced his hallucinations and frequent tinnitus. Tinnitus had been a continuous symptom since his original hospitalization.

## General Comments

Oscar's family constellation differed from that of previous cases only in the loss of his father at age seven, a factor that served to intensify the Oedipal conflict. The lost-father factor in our sample is of some interest in that *no mother* remarried.

Oscar was the second one who was able to offer a recollection that pre-dated walking. At first I tended to mistrust it, but subsequently it became apparent that these men learned to walk comparatively late and that the mastery of a secure vertical posture was more radically delayed in some cases than in others. Some did not learn to walk until they passed age two and a half, others until age four. They learned to verbalize before they learned to walk, and consequently the memories were retained.

I obtained confirmatory evidence to this effect from the study of control groups (see Chapter VII). In one such group, two subjects offered similar memories and careful interviewing revealed that neither had learned to walk until age four. Special walker devices had to be used to make them ambulatory. In one instance, the etiology vaguely indicated "weak ankles," and in the other it was unspecified, although neurological causes had been suspected.

Oscar was also the first of the group who had taken flying lessons.

His ravings on the subject of "flighting" were difficult to follow. One could not be sure of the circumstances of his "flighting" or even whether the sensations were experienced in sleep or while he was awake. Consequently, he *may* be the first of the series who "flew" in his dreams.

## THE CASE OF PHILIP

Philip was a forty-four-year-old Negro. His parents lived together during his childhood, but divorced later. They had six children, of whom Philip was the fourth. The oldest was a boy, four years older, the second a girl, three years older, the third also a girl, a year older—Philip's favorite—the fifth a boy, a year younger, and the sixth a girl, four years younger. The oldest son had been institutionalized for several years.

The father was a Canadian who had moved to America before he married. He was Catholic, but not a devout one, and allowed his children to be reared in their mother's faith, as Methodists. He seldom drank and was rarely abusive. The mother was a devout Methodist. In Philip's words, "She was a very nice woman, dedicated to her family. I know she was a schoolteacher before she married. She always did her best to help us in any way: homework, getting acquainted. She always taught us the right things to do: respect the neighbors. . . ."

His earliest memories were of motion, "red rocker, little cars, weekend bus rides in the old touring buses . . . later on, the camps with the Boy Scouts. We used to like to walk a lot, to hike." He recalled playing mostly with his siblings in the backyard. They occasionally played house at the insistence of his sisters, but he reported no sexual acts of any nature among them. "We just didn't go that way."

He was a slow student, not at all bright. He was a follower among his friends. "I was never aggressive or anything like that. I never cared for that stuff." He remembered with regret his inability to play ball in front of his peers. "I was afraid to play in front of the guys. I don't know. I played good ball, but when it came to the school team, and the gym teacher asked me to play, I turned him down. I don't know why. I did, though."

He was confused and evasive when asked about dreams. He had difficulty distinguishing between daytime activity, daydreams, and night dreams. He claimed that his night dreams usually consisted of events that had actually happened. When pressed, he told of dreaming that he was drowning. "It was really bad. I was going down, down, trying to get up, and saying, 'Why did I jump in the water like this?' " He had, however, had such an experience prior to the dream. He also remembered dreaming mostly of a monster. "I had a terror . . . I was really moving."

His best friend was a boy a year older than himself. Their favorite activities were hiking and playing baseball. He had no other significant friends.

He attended a vocational high school because it offered courses in auto mechanics. He never dated during high school. "You know, some of the guys like to be seen with girls. 'This is my girlfriend.' It never dawned on me. There was a girl I just liked. After school, a lot of the guys were running to her house. I thought, well, I would just go on home." He was terrified at the thought of talking with a girl. "She was a very nice-looking girl and I really liked her, but I never wanted to be forward and ask her to be my girlfriend, like they used to do when I was in high school. At that time it terrified me. I didn't have the nerve to do it. A couple of guys tried to pull me down to her house and ask her for a date. I don't know what I felt. I know what happened and that's the worst. I sort of wet my pants." He still hasn't gotten over the embarrassment of that experience.

He quit school after the tenth grade. He explained, "I had a problem in school. I was making passing marks, but yet the teacher left me back. I joined the State Guard at that time. I went to summer camp and I got back late in September. I reported and found I'd been left back. I knew my mark on my report card. I questioned why I was left back. My mother questioned it, but nothing was said. I quit and went to work." He denied wanting to fight his teacher,

and avoided saying he was angry. He described his reaction as
"depressed." He worked for about a year and then joined the Navy.
He was in the Navy three years and six months as a mechanic.
Philip exhibited a peculiar confusion about his age when he came
out of the Navy. He knew he was seventeen when he went in, he
knew he was in three years and six months, yet he believed himself
to have been nineteen when he came out.

He has been very religious ever since childhood. During his time
in the Navy, he usually went to church every Sunday. He denied
being religious, but later said, "You gotta obey the laws of the
Bible. Got to be. I believe in the Bible. I know what religion is. I
believe it. I go by it."

Although he was reluctant to discuss it, his first sexual experience
apparently occurred while he was in the Navy. He believed the initiative was probably on the girl's part.

After the Navy, he used the G.I. Bill to pay for flying lessons. As
a child, his favorite hobby had been building model airplanes and
flying them. He said that when he flew them, he used to dream he
was in the cockpit flying them. His descriptions of the mechanics of
piloting an aircraft were not accurate, however, and it is doubtful
that he actually obtained his pilot's license. The only excitement he
showed during interview was in connection with flying: "Ooooh,
that was the best thing! It was a strange feeling. The first time up,
it was scary." He said he wanted to be a commercial pilot, but could
give no reason why he did not continue in flying school.

Jobs were scarce, and in order to improve his training he joined
the Air Force as ground personnel. He was trained as a flight mechanic. He reported little dating activity while he was in the service.
He was in the Air Force three years and six months, also, and was
discharged when he was twenty-seven. Immediately after his discharge, he was hired by the Air Force as a civilian flight mechanic.
Soon after, he met the woman he later married, and he believed that
this period was the beginning of his troubles. She was thirty-three
when they met, separated, with three children. His description of
his first impression of her was "nice," a word he was never able to
define. "She was a nice woman. The way she presented herself, the

way she spoke. I mean, it was enticing. The way she looked, that she was nice. The way she spoke, the way she talked. To me it was nice, physically, nice person." (He described his mother in the same way.)

His wife's first husband had deserted her and his three children. She was trying to live without going on welfare. Her family had also abandoned her, and Philip felt an attraction for her and responsibility for the children almost immediately. They dated for two and a half years. They slept together during this time, not by his initiative but by "mutual agreement." He said, "She made it plain that she's not that type and her mind's not like that. She was not that type of woman. She had all the opportunity in the world. I think it's a compliment that she would never have men around the house, or strangers around. Just wasn't that way."

After these two and a half years, Philip began to feel the pressure of her problems too strongly and thought, "I'm a single man. What am I getting into? Should I continue, or what?" He broke up with her and moved to another city. He took a job as an assistant cottage manager at a training school. But he began to wonder about her, and before long, he was making weekend trips to visit her. "It was just to the point then. To me it seemed like she was about to go off the deep end. The problems had gotten so bad. She told me she couldn't stand it any longer so on my week off I said, 'Okay, I'll take you down to Washington.'" It was impossible for them to marry until her first husband had been declared legally dead, but they went through with the marriage ceremony anyway.

His wife's teenage daughter became pregnant, and soon after he lost his job. He attributed it either to the fact that he was living with a woman who was not his legal wife, or to the daughter's illegitimate pregnancy.

They moved back to their hometown, hired a lawyer, and were legally married. By this time, they had been together for nine years. Then his wife shattered him. "She tells me I never satisfied her sexually. I think she never got over sex with her first husband, William. Day in, day out, morning, noon, and night, always William." He has never been able to get over this. "The thing was always there. Kept pushing me away." The other problems continued building. "It would be out of the bed the first thing in the morning. It was like the same broken record, what the first husband did, why he didn't take care of the kids, how her family treated her."

Eventually, his wife decided she wanted a divorce. They never actually separated, but the threat was always there, and to Philip the thought of a divorce was terrifying. "It's against the Bible. I wouldn't say against the Word, but for my part I just don't think it's right. If I was divorced now, it means I should never again touch another woman."

During this troubled period, the patient was working two jobs. "Anything to stay out of the house to have peace and quiet." He was a flight mechanic for a commercial airline, and he was driving for a car rental service. He began to experience dissociative episodes while driving. "I'd been living around there all of my life. Places I'd know blindfolded, I couldn't find my way in and I couldn't find my way out. Like sometimes I'd go to work, I'd get on the bus, and I'd wind up and find myself where I shouldn't be."

Unable to stand the strain any longer, he packed and flew to Jamaica. He was there about two weeks. While there, he said, "Felt like somebody was after me or people were after me. I don't know, didn't want anybody around. What's wrong with me? I never could understand what she meant. Afraid to be around people. Gotta keep moving, find some place where it's safe." Deciding it was not safe in Jamaica, he went to the airport to go home. Apparently, he became completely disoriented there. The events took on a dream-like quality and he remembered only pieces of what happened. "I felt so sick. I remember all that night everybody was chasing me. It seemed there was nobody in the lobby, nobody in the airfield. I had to keep moving. I got to get home. And I kept getting the fear." He managed to get on a plane, but was still confused. "I heard their voices. I could hear myself yelling, 'What is everybody doing to me, what is everybody doing to me?'" The next thing he remembered was being in the police station.

Events at the station were sketchy in his mind. He was horrified to learn that he was being held for attempted skyjacking. "I said,

'No, no, no, no!' " He was often lost in moving around the jail and failed to recognize prisoners with whom he had shared cells.

He stated that his fear of people was subsiding and that he was anxious to return home.

## General Comments

The only factor of unusual importance here is Philip's extremely high level of directional confusion associated with lateral movement. (In this respect he is closest to Brian and Elmer.) It is continuously interesting to me how these men first become upset on a vertical affective axis, and how subsequently the lateral axis becomes involved through direct action, and how it then becomes disoriented by angular rotation.

It might also be pertinent to note that the paralytic elements in Philip's dream activity did not resolve into dreams of flight, and that, by the same token, he was not engaged in criminal activity. His religious faith has never wavered, as is true of the others who were "non-flying" as well as non-criminal. His father image was the least violent one of the sample, which manifested itself in the fact that he had no gun at the time of the alleged offense.

## THE CASE OF RONALD

Ronald was thirty-two, the second of five children. He had a brother three years younger, a brother eleven years younger, and a sister fourteen years younger.

The father was engaged in the ownership of service-sales businesses. During periods when he was between businesses or trying other jobs, the famiy security was often jeopardized. During the patient's childhood, the father was "drunk most of the time, had a very vile temper. About all we had to look forward to when we saw him—which was rare—was getting a beating."

The oldest son was obviously his father's favorite. "He got the best clothes. When he was in grade school, my father bought him a motorcycle, and when he was in high school, he bought him a new convertible." This brother is still dependent on the father, and unable to keep a job. In regard to his own relationship with his father, Ronald said, "My older brother told me that my dad didn't care for me. When I told my father this—I don't know if he was drunk or not—he said, 'Yes, that's right. I hate you. I wish you were dead.' This is pretty strong stuff for a kid."

The mother was very high-strung. "My mother was always screaming." She screamed at the children and at their father for "drinking and running around with other women." Nevertheless, Ronald described her as a "very religious person." She took the children to Sunday School regularly where he learned "to live your life as if Jesus were right beside you. There was nothing wrong that I would do. I would not tell a lie even if somebody was going to kill me. Then I got a beating from my father one day for something I did not do and he insisted that I had done it and was lying. I said, 'All right, I never told a lie, but it's not doing me any good, so I'm going to start lying like everybody else.' " The mother believed in Heaven and Hell and passed her belief on to her children. Ronald remembered believing that almost anything would send a person to Hell, such as "jaywalking or picking your nose."

His earliest memory was of lying in a crib and watching his mother's shadow on a wall. This was before he could walk. Other early memories were of a fishing expedition and other outings. As far back as he could remember, he has had dreams of flying, "mostly over a desert or a wilderness, stream, or forest, and I can go anywhere I want. I'm actually flapping my arms. Sometimes if I want altitude I have to make swimming motions." (He made swimming motions as he talked.) These dreams were still occurring. He also reported dreams "where somebody was chasing me and I felt like I was running on a treadmill or in deep sand and I couldn't get going." This dream frequently preceded the dream of flight.

The mother depended heavily on Ronald for emotional relief. He recalled that she often put the children in the car and drove for miles and miles when she was upset. Later, he developed the same dependence on driving; he claimed that he was in his car "constantly," and that driving gave him "a sense of freedom."

He was a poor student and often truant from the first grade on. "They would just pass me because I was getting older than the other kids." He quit school when he was sixteen.

Part of his reason for dropping out of school was his social maladjustment. He did not participate in sports. He was "scared to death of girls, very, very bashful. Couldn't talk to them, too shy." He couldn't date "because I didn't get along with girls. I didn't get along in class at school. I couldn't get along in a place like that, so I'd walk around with my head down. If somebody'd speak to me, I wouldn't speak back. Yet, after school was out, me and a friend might go over to a girl's house and spend a couple of hours and get along fine."

Ronald had his first sexual experience at age seven when his mother's fourteen-year-old sister "wanted me to screw her. I didn't get anything out of it because I was so young. I just didn't get anything out of it. I laid down and she laid on top of me." After he quit school, he had a brief affair with a girl his own age. "I guess you could say she seduced me. We were laying on the couch with a blanket over us and she kept saying she didn't want to do it. I knew that wasn't true because she pulled her own pants off. She said she didn't want to do it. Anyway, we did." He frequented prostitutes while in the Marines.

He joined the Marines at age seventeen and was discharged after serving a full term. When he enlisted, he was very religious, but he claimed to have lost his religion in the service because of the death of his grandfather. "I was praying so hard that he would be all right until I got home. That's when my prayers weren't answered, I felt let down." Apparently, this grandfather was much more of a father to him during his childhood than his father was. He believed that his prayers could save the old man, and when they didn't, he had the same feeling he had when he decided to lie because it did no good not to lie. He began "drinking like a fish" at that time.

While in the Marines, he learned to fly. He took private lessons.

He described flying as giving him "a feeling of well-being, enjoying myself very much." Being on the deck of a ship during a storm, riding a motorcycle up and down hills, skin diving—all these gave him this feeling. He still had occasional dreams of paralysis.

He spent six months in a psychiatric hospital after a suicide effort. After the Marines, he was not able to hold a steady job. "A couple of months I'd say would be the average." He usually quit because he was afraid his employers were planning to fire him. "I think the boss or bosses are looking for somebody to replace me and plotting against me to get me out of the job and that I'll quit before they can fire me." He felt like a compete failure. "I use the term 'failure' because I'm thirty-two years old and I've never held a steady job. I have no talent to speak of. There's nothing I do well enough to earn me a living—no savings—I have no future. As far as I'm concerned, that's a failure."

Just after coming out of the Marines, he began living with a woman who subsequently became pregnant. They moved back to his hometown and lived together for several years. Two children were born to them. Although he offered to marry her several times, she refused. They were settled down. "We had a nice brick house in a nice neighborhood, paved streets, beautiful neighborhood—a real nice house. We just had the two children and I was making pretty good money." Suddenly, she left him for another man and took the children with her. This desertion shattered his dreams of stability. He quit his job and bought his own business. The thin veneer of belief in his sexual desirability and competence was destroyed also.

Then he started seeing another woman; they dated about a month, got married, and lived together for all of two weeks. He considered it a "business proposition" through which he hoped to get his children back, but it failed. At this point, he was behaving like his father. He drank, ran around with other women, and owned a business. He did not engage in criminal activity.

He filed for divorce and began living with another woman. This woman became pregnant and left him, although he offered to marry her as soon as he was free. She started a paternity suit against him which utterly bewildered him, since he was perfectly willing to accept and support the child. He was never allowed to see the child, and he felt bad about that.

He married his present wife soon afterward. "Love at first sight. Crazy about her, we really fell in love." She was a go-go dancer in a bar.

By this time, he had given up his business and was operating one for his father. It was in financial difficulty when he took it over. He added new services to the business, worked from 6 A.M. to midnight, seven days a week. It began paying off. "We were doing so much business, we had five or six men on a shift. The money was rolling in. My father went out and bought a new car for himself, a new car for my mother, a new car for my brother. It was heaven." However elated he was over his success, he was having trouble. "He was paying me, splitting the new services, and $150 a week. It was good money, but I had to work over a hundred hours a week for that money and no home life. My wife bitched all the time. Then my old man began telling my wife I wasn't doing my job. I thought, 'I'm making too much money. He wants to get rid of me.' " The father frequently cheated on the division of the new services' profits, constantly interfered with hiring and firing, and refused Ronald any time off or to allow any of his own employees to help out at peak periods. He complained to everyone in the family that in spite of tremendous profits, Ronald was not doing an effective job. Finally, Ronald threatened to quit unless he had a few hours off. The next day, he found that his younger brother had taken over as manager and he was fired.

He admitted strong murderous impulses toward his father. "I told my brother, 'I've got some money coming. If he tries to keep so much as a dollar of it, I'll shoot him. I'll take my gun down there to pick up the check and if he says so much as a word or takes so much as a dollar out of my check, I'll blow him in two.' "

For about two months, he was quite despondent. He lay around all day and did nothing. "I was down physically and mentally because I had been taking pills, pep pills, to get me going when I was working at the station. When I quit, I was in pretty bad shape. I was terribly tired. I would sleep the whole day through." His wife was pregnant. She urged him to get a job and he found one as a railroad switchman. At this time, his wife told him she had been two-timing him before they were married. "I told her she should have told me this before we married. I said I didn't know if it would have made any difference or not. At this point, I felt that she should have told me. I was hurt and I'm still hurt by it." They quarreled and she left him.

He began to consider skyjacking. "I had no great desire to go to Cuba. I think I pretty much fell into a position where everything would be taken out of my hands and solved for me, everything for better or worse, because it'd be out my hands." He picked up his son by his first wife and brought him home. He called his present wife and fought with her again. Then he left for the airport with his son and they boarded a plane bound for Miami. He had a broken-down shotgun in his suitcase. He waited until midflight to assemble it. Then, after the plane was already making its landing approach, "I called the stewardess back and showed her the shotgun, told her to tell the captain to take us to Havana. She went up to the cabin. We were up about a thousand feet, I think they said. I don't think I really wanted to do it. If I was going to skyjack a plane, I certainly wouldn't do it at a thousand feet altitude."

During the interview, Ronald made no effort to excuse his crime. Rather, he said, "I really believe sincerely that I'm a social misfit, and I think I need some kind of guidance. I've had a terrible life and I've been unhappy most of it. I think a person deserves better that that."

### General Comments

In addition to the familiar factors, I was interested by the high level of consistency between Ronald's desires which he sought to satisfy in his daily activities (flying, driving, sailing, skin diving, etc.) and the vigor of his nocturnal dreams of flight.

Here is another instance where the first memory comes from the period preceding walking ability. In every case, when such a memory was introduced during the study, it was gratuitously "thrust" into the interview by the patient: it was not until the interviews were almost complete that I began to realize what was being repeatedly told to me.

Ronald's case throws into relief a factor that persists throughout the sample, namely, the early forcible introduction to sexual experience by an older woman. Perhaps a man cannot be *raped,* but he certainly can be compelled and humiliated by an older woman. These men may have a coveted little sister, but they were actually *had* by older relatives and friends.

Ronald may have been more active sexually than many of the others, still he tended to turn to the same types of women—prostitutes, go-go girls, etc.

# VII

## Retrojection

By now, the readers of this volume should be well aware of the repeated frequency with which the son of a bully becomes a mouse and remains one until such time that his father is incapacitated.

At this point, it often appears that although the patient is consciously pleased at his father's departure, he later is somehow less stable. When, sometime later, his life falls into shambles, the boy suddenly abandons the feminine guise he has worn for years and, in a single violent moment, becomes the exact embodiment of his detested father.

Of course, the question would logically follow: Do women ever respond in this same way? The answer is yes.

In order to expain a word that will be used in the volume beyond this point, I would like to tell you of a young woman. The clarity of her process will, I believe help.

### THE CASE OF JANE

Twelve years ago, I interviewed a sixteen-year-old female resident of a state custodial institution.

She had previously lived with her grandmother. Her birth was illegitimate (a by-product of her mother's rebellious high living) and constituted a handicap to her mother's movement. The grandmother, a psychopath herself, had earlier driven her own daughter into the streets with harsh Christian punitiveness. She hated her grandchild and saw in her the embodiment of all evil.

During the patient's earlier years (clearly between the ages of two and six), the grandmother was often angry at the disobedience of the child. At such moments, she threw her to the floor, shouting imprecations relative to the child's badness, evilness, bastardy, cowardliness, and lack of character. She stomped with her shoe heels upon the child, who, full of self-detestation, hate, and desperation, had cried, pleaded, crawled and finally acknowledged her grandmother's imprecations. At five or six the child found ways to make partial peace with the grandmother, which prevented the continuance of these experiences. They lived together several years longer, until the grandmother died. At this point, the child was removed to a state home.

At interview, it was apparent she was a very sick girl with a shattered ego, in which nominal cathexis was not working adequately. The most deeply buried parts of her being lay poorly disguised, with their connections and cathexes showing. She was so emotionally ill that she was aware of aspects of herself which the ordinary person would successfully conceal from themselves and others.

Her symptomatic behavior had appeared at age fourteen, while caring for younger children. She had become increasingly withdrawn, with evidence of mounting tension. These periods were climaxed by violent episodes. She would throw children to the floor and stomp them with her heels while shouting vicious accusations.

She explained her problem quite simply, saying that she felt she was bad, she was stupid, she was a bastard, she was a coward —look how she crawled. At first, these feelings and audible recollections seemed like external visitations for which she had no clear reference. Three months after their beginning, however, she suddenly recalled (while experiencing these feelings and hearing these voices) clear visual images of her grandmother's kitchen and image.

On several occasions during such recollections, she had suddenly felt sharp pains at various points on her back. She remembered tissues being broken, torn by the heels of her grandmother's shoes. It seemed *so real,* she asked her roommates, and subsequently the doctor, to examine her back. There *were* scars in each of these areas. She had no previous conscious recollection of their existence. As the intensity and duration of her feelings increased, so too did the seemingly real character of the sensations. Unlike the neurotic who says, "It seemed as if . . . ," she experienced the clear sensation, "Grandmother *is* kicking me," "I *am* bad," and "I *am* awful." She believed her grandmother was physically *putting these feelings into her.*

She believed that these "bad feelings" were flowing *into her* through grandmother's heels. It appeared likely to her that, if she could stomp upon another person in this same fashion, the bad feelings would physically and literally flow down her own legs and through her heels, *into the victim.* Thus, she could be rid of the feelings. Shortly thereafter, for the first time, she actually did physically beat and stomp a child. She said in interview that, for the moment, there was some gratification and discharge of feeling from her own person. The effect lasted about twenty-four hours, but was followed by a gradual return of the same feelings. Several weeks were required before the intensity of her feelings was again sufficient to demand discharge.

## DISCUSSION

This mechanism is the mental device that I should like to call *retrojection.* In one form or another, it is very common to human behavior. The fact that this form of behavior was given a legal status in man's earliest law codes and that it finds itself expressed in the form of behavior of children and nations today, suggests that it deserves better treatment from psychiatry than it has had to date. It should not be confused with introjection, projection, or identification, each of which have their own specific meanings. It is a commonly observed phenomenon in the behavior of bullies.

The phenomenon of retrojection has been gradually clarified for me by further observations of other instances in which such clear-cut cathexes have not always been as well demonstrated, but where the obvious "eye-for-an-eye and tooth-for-a-tooth" character of behavior has been as evident. The behavior or ideation which is retrojected must ideally cause in the new victim *exactly the same feelings* formerly produced in the original victim.

There is one aspect of retrojection that must be carefully clarified. In the early historical developmental sequence of every individual, there is an opportunity at the appropriate age to learn this particular mechanism, but it does not necessarily hold that the mechanism will be used to any significant degree in healthy individuals, until such time as events transpire in which its use as a principle of defense is desperately required. At such a moment, the more reasonable ego defenses will ordinarily already be in shambles. In other instances, the mechanism will be subtly woven into the character and will not suddenly 'break through."

An introject must inevitably be a schematic mental representation involving both a physical image and an emotional content deriving from previous experience, with an individual who has been particularly frustrating, i.e., introjected. I wonder if it may not be true that identification is chiefly conscious (or readily brought into consciousness by interpretation), and that it is based upon the mental representation of the "good mother" and the "good father." To go further, I believe that the image of "good mother," "good father," closely corresponds with the gratified id demands, and that in time it comes to be encapsulated within the conscious ethical system of the individual, and is, therefore, part of ego.

On the other hand, I have never encountered a troublesome introject which resembled anything other than the obverse image of the "good parent," i.e., the "bad parent" or "bad image." For the moment, I am tempted to say all introjects thus stem from the "bad" (displeasing) figure. To the extent that an introject represents the "bad," the frustrating, so indeed does it *represent the negative aspect of the indifference of our natural environment,* and thus it is patterned upon, and acquires the characteristics of, one's personal relationship to the gravitational force, and belongs to superego.

At this point, I should like to point out that *the concept of intro-*

*jection, of "taking into one's own person an alien aspect of the external environment," is almost exactly met by one physical structure: the otoconia of the inner ear.* It is precisely an introject. It is a tiny, internal, ever-present physical representative of the external force, gravity. In point of fact, were there no gravity, there would be no discharge of electropotential in the endothelium over which it was formed and now lies.

I am arguing that the otoconia, and the physical sensations and emotions derived from it, is precisely the precursor of superego function and provides the pattern for the creation and management of emotional introjects, which are a part of superego. Alexander often described the psychoanalytic procedure as a "corrective emotional experience" through which it was the intention of the therapist to extirpate a previous introject and to replace it with a gentler and less frustrating figure with which the patient can live in greater harmony.

In a sense, this young lady was attempting to be her own psychological surgeon. It was her intention to remove the painfully incorporated mental image from her past by means of a psychotic physical mechanism through her heels.

Every individual in his ontopsychogenic development passes through a period in which it is consistent with his understanding of life to learn the mechanism of retrojection.

The mechanism becomes significant in those moments of stress in which the intensity of internal sensation is such that only by discharging its cathexis can one reactivate homeostatic balance. I am suggesting that, at such times of emergency, a whole ego state with its specific, related superego companion is liberated to meet the emergency.

Thus, it it conceivable that a single individual, marked repeatedly, continuously, and deeply by a repetitive, frustrating experience with a significant individual in his existence, would, as a child, effect an identification with another, more pleasing figure and yet introjects the image of the frustrating person, which would later be retrojected at critical moments *without his conscious awareness or control.*

Since I first began to use the term retrojection for understanding some of the invisible sabotage in interpersonal relationships, it has often been decisive in my understanding of some of the minutiae of the personal relationship between patients and myself. In consultation, there often occur brief, strained moments between us that are perceptible either through amost unnoticeable pauses, or word inflection, or ideational range, or body movement on their part that reflect an experience they had had with a frustrating parent. Generally, the patient is unaware of his maneuvers, but they constitute a direct playback of typical situations with the frustrating parent. In the playback, however, the roles are reversed so that *they* play the part of the frustrating parent, and *I am supposed to react* with feelings of embarrassment, rejection, or other unpleasant sensations that they had felt at the hands of this same parent. Ultimately, it usually appeared that the hidden mechanics of retrojection had been a chief factor in their interpersonal failures. They knew they had failed, but were without understanding of the cause.

In almost every case of this type that I have seen, the patient feels very differently about his two parents. One parent he idolizes and consciously copies. He consciously believes he is like that parent. The other parent he despises and vows he will never be like that one. He denies any similarity to the hated parent, and yet, the hateful aspects of that parent are inextricably wound up in *his* failures, overcompensate as he will to conceal it. His surface personality is like that of the individual with whom he has identified. The unconscious, but highly determinative, figure is, however, present as an *introject* that he cannot see, and whose *retrojection* he cannot understand. In fact, he usually has countless overcompensations upon which to base the rationalization that he has rejected the hated figure. Frequently, so much of his energy is involved in such overcompensations and denials that he is virtually paralyzed by ineffectiveness, as were the first two skyjackers.

In the course of most human lives, an introject (if there be any) is usually so deeply buried as to be no source of problem except in characterological manifestations. Given a certain amount of ego damage or threat, an introject shows up, first, as a *projection* in which one fears in others the destructive element in oneself and, given further ego damage, the introject bursts through undiluted as a *retrojection*. When it appears, it always wears a garb of finality and absolutism, of inevitability and indifference exactly like that of gravity itself. The assassin simply states of his action, "That's the way it had to be."

The "wild moment" in which these individuals skyjacked air-craft would best be described as the mechanisms of retrojection. The original father figure, violent and cruel, was the one that was originally accepted by the boys. This acceptance occurred in the period of time in which the highest level of psychic and ethical de-velopment of the children was equal to that of the average adult at the time of Hammurabi. At that time, "Might made right," and the *lex talionis* held sway.

As these boys passed the age of five, due to their exposure to the Christian (so-called) ethical principle of the importance of love, as opposed to violence, they identified themselves with their mother's values and repressed from their conscious personalities the use of violence, or threats of violence, to force their wills upon another. This identification with the maternal role in its exaggerated and helpless form led ultimately to their failures, precipitating a series of experiences that were humiliatingly dissociative. These final humiliating experiences were depersonalizing and stripped away the last vestiges of a thirty-year accumulation of passivity (accumulated overcompensation). In the particular moment in which, gun in hand, they did violence to the hostess, each was the retrojected image of his own previously introjected father. Only at a highly critical moment would they dare this previously "impos-sible" thing.

The word *rape* is a powerful one, but unfortunately in the lay and legal world it is often restricted to the forceful introjection of one's own body into that of an unwilling other. It would be wise if we were to understand that the unpleasant emotional experiences and the ultimate consequences of one individual's being used forcibly by another are as great as rape, and are, in fact, identical with rape whether physical penetration occurs or not. Thus, a male can be raped as readily as a female *and with comparable damage*. Introjection is psychological rape.

Granting a mutuality of emotion, the penetration by one of another, who willingly receives, is the highest order of mutuality and of humanity. The introduction of force instantly converts the highest to the lowest, as is consistently noted in the common forms of expression currently being employed on our occupied college campuses and in our burning cities. Here the ultimate insult hurled from behind the barricades is summed up in the words, "get screwed" and "fuck you." These are individuals who, whether justified or not, feel themselves to have been *used* in multiple ways that did not involve physical penetration, but who offer that act as a retaliation upon those who they feel have "shafted them." Retrojection is their mechanism and it involves interesting aspects of inevitability, finality, willingness for fatality, as well as the negativism that, "What goes up, must come down."

In this particular time of social upheaval and unrest, there are many who feel that they have been used and who seek to redress their feeling through actions that, like skyjacking, carry for them the symbolic contempt of rape and involve retrojection. In the ultimate form, a consistent retrojection, through human expression, would be nihilism, in which man, imitating the indifference of his environment, would destroy his institutions, just as gravity would destroy his structures. It is particularly characteristic of retrojection to be "an all or nothing" proposition. It always has about it the air of ultimate inevitability.

As boys, these fellows matured in the presence of a violent father who did, in fact (and probably with the knowledge of the children), forcibly use the mother sexually. This same disregard for the interest and welfare of every other member of the family was undoubtedly expressed by the father. In a sense, then, every member of such a family was continuously "raped" by that violent figure.[1]

So it is today. The expression, "to get even (rape)," is com-

---

[1] In recent years in connection with the "battered child syndrome," there have been numerous attempts to answer the question, "Does violence beget violence"? As far as the material with which we have been dealing is concerned, the data clearly depict parents who, in their own childhoods, were victims of violent parents and who, in their own child-raising, do "as they have been done unto."

monly used. It is to be seen in its purest form when the intent of
the retaliation of the one who supposes himself to have been victimized is to reduplicate exactly in his aggressor those uncomfortable feelings previously produced in himself. In its less pure and
more common form, a symbolic substitute is acceptable. In the
latter instance, "any woman" could be "scaped," or could serve as
the substitute object of revenge, or in an even less specific form
"any other member, all other members of the human race" could
stand to be "scaped" as a substitute for the self in externalizing
(retrojecting) previous experience, particularly if that "other"
could be symbolically associated in the mind of the victim with
the source of his pain or humiliation. A "scaped" airline pilot is
not a poor substitute for an astronaut, nor a "scaped" hostess a
poor substitute for a mother or little sister.

Perhaps the development of a single individual human after
birth includes not only those experiences that are related to his own
more recent ancestors, but in addition those which occurred to his
earlier predecessors who did not have our complicated cerebral
equipment. Perhaps these experiences also occur, even today,
among lower life forms such as dogs, birds, cattle, reptiles, etc.,
so that there is extant among them and us a certain common reality
system which stems not from a complex and variable human meta-
psychology, but which is consistent with the physical world and
the physical forces which dominate it. I believe that this is in fact
demonstrable.

If ontopsychogenesis recapitulates cognigenesis, then it would
suggest one's earliest experiences are sub-human or mammalian in
character and that only later do they assume a more nearly interpersonal or human value.

This is the moment to explain the footnote in Chapter II, page
36, in which reference is made to a child's seeing his father as
"the first figure capable of defeating gravity." What is meant, actually, is that he is the first and strongest primarily *interpersonal*
figure. The mother, obviously, comes *first* in the life of a child. Her
relationship is so early, so basic that she is, however, originally
(like the earth) indistinguishable from himself. She occurs to him

first as an intrapsychic part of his own person, from which he later separates himself. This "oneness" is referred to as primary identification. At the time (somewhere after a year) that he clearly sees himself as separate from her, the father begins to enter his mental picture. Thus, *at that moment* he is aware of the father's *greater* physical strength and is able to identify that characteristic with the father.

Thus, the mother object (ideal and giving) stands in contrast to the father (strong and demanding). Perhaps this is why we refer to mother earth (succor and aid) and fatherland (discipline and demands).

# VIII

## The Case of Sam

Sam was thirty-six years old. His parents were born within twenty miles of their present home and both came from families that had been settled in the area for three to five generations and had achieved approximately identical economic, social, educational, and moral standards of life. The marital relationship was apparently good, unmarked by violence.

Sam described his father as a "good, church-going man, a Lutheran." He said his mother's people were Baptists. (The religious definition was his first descriptive term for both.) He further described his father as being a large man and as being "always pretty understanding, with no difficulties. He did everything in the world for me, financially, and in the way of understanding." The father originally worked for his brother in his business. He was frugal, and in time he purchased a half-interest in a profitable business of which he became the sole owner. The business was large, and Sam had been working for his father for six years.

The mother was described as rather emotional, particularly after the death by leukemia of Sam's little sister at the age of six. Sam was nine at the time. The mother has been having heart trouble ever since, and has also had several operations, including the removal of a breast.

Sam recalled more about his mother than about his father, who was generally working, except on weekends. Weekends were devoted to visits with the maternal and paternal grandparents.

He characterized his mother as "a stickler for everything, you know, squared away in the house, and the house being clean."

His mother wrote the rules and they were not extremely strict. She did not want him too dirty, just average, so that he was not clean enough to be teased by other children. The father took care of the discipline. The patient was closer to his mother than to his father. In the early years, the father was perhaps closer to the sister than to the boy.

He recalled no sibling rivalry. He remembered such things as tricycles, etc., and the funeral of the little girl. He recalled that she was mostly in the house with the mother.

Apparently, Sam was treated rather strictly, but not without a fair amount of permissiveness. He was allowed to do things he wanted to do "which were all right," but by the same token, the things he wanted to do were "all right" to begin with. His mother was obviously ambitious for him, but willing to let him achieve in such fashion as was possible for him. His recollections of his first day in school were of having a fight that an older boy started but that he finished. His grades in school were average. He attended public school through junior high school, then went to a parochial high school. He was physically quite capable throughout school. He lettered in football, and later played basketball on scholarship at a junior college.

He had little recollection of dreams and less of nightmares, except for one in which the Devil was chasing him around. He recalled that he as well as almost everyone else was preoccupied with religion, and that he was full of questions about this subject. He was duly confirmed, went to catechism class, etc. He asked many questions about "why" he was required to perform these duties. In addition to his Lutheran training, which was consistent with the upbringing of his father, he also went to the Baptist church Sunday nights with his mother and grandmother.

The grandmother was described as a "rather fair person, who liked everything squared away in the house, clothes cleaned. She didn't want kids messing things up."

In school, Sam was usually a member of a peer group, not a loner. He felt that his acceptance by his classmates was average. He began to date at sixteen or seventeen, although apparently infrequently. He ran around with a gang of boys who might go by a girl's house, but did not date steadily. His introduction to sex took place in his sixteenth year, although he had known about it since age twelve. When he was eight, he was part of the usual play between children; he and another boy engaged in sexual exploration with girls older than themselves, in which the girls were the instigators. He was never caught in this activity, but he was aware that his parents "knew what was going on." He was fearful of them and stopped it as soon as possible.

His first sexual experience resulted from advances made by a girl who was older than himself. Afterward, he suffered from fear and concern, even though he was unaware of the risk of pregnancy or disease. It was simply a moral matter which bothered him for some time. Comparable experiences continued to occur about once a year, always through the aggression of an older girl.

At high school, he "didn't date at all. It just didn't seem like the thing I had to do." He took part in school activities, met girls at the dances, and responded to those who were aggressive toward him. At seventeen, he met the girl who was to become his bride. She was fourteen, but she was the aggressor who solidified the relationship.

He graduated from high school and was mobilized into the Air National Guard. During his eighteen months of active service, he was a guard at various nuclear installations. His bride-to-be corresponded with him regularly. After his discharge, he enrolled at a college and played basketball on scholarship. By then, his relationship with his girl had become sexual and remained so up until their marriage. He felt that sexual activity made the relationship "easier." She did not seem troubled by it, and thus it tended to strengthen their bond. They married a year after he started college.

He dropped out of school, rented an apartment, and went to work in a service station for three months. Then he got a job with the telephone company and remained for eight and a half years, achieving a series of promotions. Three children were born to the marriage during that time, but at this juncture he went to work for his father who had acquired the business by then and wished to have his son work with him.

His assumption that things would go well between himself and his father proved to be correct. During our interview, he still regarded the relationship as good, in spite of the state of affairs. He planned to return to work with his father.

Sam had been in the Air National Guard for some ten years after leaving college. Then he transferred to a Marine air reserve unit, several years after most of his friends and associates had done so. He felt somehow ashamed about it even though he knew it was not his fault, as there were no vacancies in the unit when he first volunteered. Most of his friends took a three-year enlistment and served in the Korean war.

Sam took up parachute jumping as a civilian and continued it as a member of the Marine reserve unit. He put a great deal of effort into the reserves and achieved an outstanding performance record. He earned meritorious promotions and letters of commendation.

Sam had been experiencing a certain amount of discomfort from a long-standing condition of his left eyelid. Originally, his eye was infected by a rose thorn when he was ten. Corrective surgery was attempted several times, but each operation made matters worse. The eye was infected again during his stay in Cuba, and at the time of our interview, the droopy eyelid lent his face a rather characteristic appearance.

Sam and his wife have been married for sixteen years. His description of her left the impression of a vigorous woman of strong temper, who expresses herself without difficulty. Their disagreements have been tempered with consideration, and the relationship has been good throughout. They had four children, a daughter of fifteen, a boy of thirteen, a boy of nine, and a girl of three.

Sam broke an ankle on a parachute jump, but continued to jump in spite of the fact that he was wearing a cast. As a result of favoring the ankle, he fell frequently and sustained a number of severe concussions. He was knocked unconscious at least three times. On one such occasion, when asked who he was, he replied, "Flash Gordon!"

In mid-December, 1968, he received a severe blow on the head from a machine with which he was working. It struck him over the right eye and required a number of stitches. He saw the doctor a number of times. Two weeks following that event, a former reservist who once saved Sam's life (after one of his ill-advised jumps) returned to Vietnam. Sam experienced much emotional turmoil about it. He turned confused and meditative because others seemed to have duties and take risks while he was spared. He reacted strongly to news about the *Pueblo,* and when he saw a television program which reported the strong pro-Cuban sentiments of a formerly Southern girl, it angered and irritated him greatly. He experienced greater and greater emotion and began to cry, which was most unusual for him. He took to sitting alone in a warehouse at work. He felt sorry for himself, envious of his buddies, and angry at the Communists. He was embarrassed for fear his children would see him crying. He continued his parachute jumps with much bravado. His family was quite concerned about him, especially his father, who suggested that it might be necessary for him to be hospitalized.

On a Sunday afternoon, a week before his skyjacking, he became suddenly enraged at his thirteen-year-old boy who had accidentally discharged a shotgun in the home. He was especially furious because the boy was always cautious in the use of firearms. Yet, in this instance he might have accidentally killed his little sister. Sam spanked the boy extremely hard and "said things to him I should not have said." He was aware of murderous feelings toward the boy. They passed by the next day, but his guilt at having experienced them was intense. From Monday through Friday of that week, he was more isolated than usual. He spent more time in the warehouse alone, brooding over his angry thoughts toward his son. He resented his failure as a man and his lack of active military experience.

On Saturday morning he did the usual payroll chore, but became increasingly angry at the incompetence, dependence, and ignorance of the employees toward whom he felt like a social worker. This role contrasted poorly with the valorous acts of his friend. At noon, they closed the store and he made a delivery. He sat with a friend and had several beers. When he left, he did not want to go home because of his fear that his children would notice his emotional state. He sat brooding alone until dark. Then he drove home and told his wife that he wanted her to take him to town. He told her he was going to Cuba, that secrecy was involved in this matter, but he had been instructed to kill Castro. He called a friend, a captain in the reserve, and asked him if he would take him to the airport. The captain said he would. En route, Sam borrowed a .45 automatic. He explained to the captain that the CIA planned to assassinate Fidel Castro, that it was his assignment, and he would fulfill it. In his own mind, he did not think he would be able to kill Castro with the gun he had acquired. He planned to use it simply to skyjack the airplane. Eventually, when he got close to Castro, he would grab a gun from a guard and use that weapon.

He took a plane en route to Miami, his automatic in his Army reserve briefcase. Very gently, he asked a passenger, "Do you mind going by way of Cuba?" Then, he knocked softly on the cabin door and asked the same question of the crew. The crew received him with smiles, assuring him of their willingness to comply with his every order.

He inquired if there was sufficient gasoline to make the flight without danger, if the weather ahead was satisfactory, and if there would be a scramble by North American Air Defense that might cause complications. The crew reassured him in these matters. He also inquired about Havana airport and whether that particular plane could land there without risks or complications.

He asked the hostess for a drink and she promptly complied. While he drank, he handed his gun to the flight engineer. The engineer handed it back when Sam finished his drink, and he placed it in his lap as they approached Havana. During the approach, while expressing concern for the inconvenience to his fellow passengers, he mentioned that if he had his parachute with him he would be glad to jump, making it unnecessary for the plane to land. When it did land, he opened the door while the plane was still rolling, placed his gun on the floor at the feet of the pilot, and prepared to depart. At that point, the Captain asked him, "Are you sure this is what you want to do?" When Sam jumped from the plane, he had no arms with him. He was apprehended and his papers were examined. Among others, he carried his Armed Forces ID, his Masonic and Shrine cards. He immediately asked to be taken to Fidel, but the soldiers only laughed. He did not tell them why he wanted to get to Castro. He was kept in custody for 107 days, after which the Cubans sent him to Canada. When he arrived there, he promptly turned himself over to the U.S. Embassy, like the proper and obedient boy that he was. He declared that he was a skyjacker and all he wanted to do was go home to face his problem and get it over with. He was sent back to court, where he was remanded to a facility for examination.

## DISCUSSION OF SAM

The importance of this case is the subtlety of process. Unlike most of the others, Sam is large physically, and has an excellent record of neuromotor activity.

In addition, unless one states categorically that Germanic fathers (or most fathers) represent force and violence, it is more difficult to create the image of a hostile border between him and his wife. The probable severity of her grief and its effects on her personality are some help, though.

Dreams of paralysis and flight are absent if one is willing to overlook the one in which he is chased by the Devil. The only clear evidence of neurotic involvement with space appears in the intensity of his interest in parachuting, which obviously was used to bolster his self-image.

Then, a sharp blow to the head, followed by depression and the sudden precipitous act. Even there, his self-control was greater, as manifested by his concern for fellow passengers.

It seems clear he would not have skyjacked had he not been injured. Is it possible that some head injuries might produce severe physiologic disruption or pathology in the equilibratory mechanism? Two other skyjackers gave histories of head injury. Brian experienced one early in his illness and Dan did so as a boy, after which he felt he was "someone else." He will be described in a later chapter.

### Judicial Aftermath

Sam's case probably caused more trouble between the Department of Justice and myself than did any other. Accordingly, this is

the ideal juncture for me to single out most emphatically the insup-
portable stance assumed by the Department in the prosecution of
skyjackers. In the first place, no "successful" skyjacker has ever
been apprehended by the efforts of the Department and brought to
trial. Even the "unsuccessful" ones could not have been apprehended had they not chosen to surrender as the result of some sort
of persuasion, while the "successful" ones returned voluntarily to
the United States in full awareness of having to stand trial for a
capital offense. In brief, every skyjacker who goes on trial does so
by his own choice, and decidedly not by the accomplishment of
the Department. Nevertheless, every returning skyjacker has a
$100,000 bail slapped on him, which effectively prevents him from
preparing an adequate defense.

The trouble with Sam was that he could afford to engage his
own lawyers and even manage to make bail, in contrast to all but
one of the other skyjackers who had to make do with court-
appointed defenders. (The exception was a Texas oilman with his
own lawyer who got off with a $100 fine and a lecture after con-
vincing the court that the alcohol served to him by the airline had
produced his bizarre behavior.)

Sam's defense subpoenaed psychiatrists and neurologists for the
trial. One of them was in private practice nearby: Dr. C. H. Thig-
pen, the nationally known author of *The Three Faces of Eve*. Also
subpoenaed were Harold Fain, Assistant Chief of Psychiatry at the
federal hospital, and mysef as consultant to that facility.

The case, more than any other, demonstrated the bull-headed,
blindered approach of Justice's Division of Prosecution. After Sam
had been studied at the hospital, the consensus was that he was now
sane and could stand trial, but that at the time of the crime he had
not been in full possession of his faculties, due to injury. Although
the court's interest was limited to Sam's current condition, it took
cognizance of the contents of the report. The prosecuting attorney
contacted Washington and said, in effect, "We can't win, let's drop
the charge." Washington, however, knew better and insisted. The
change of administrations was about to take place, and the in-
cumbent U.S. Attorney let the matter ride so that it could be
dumped into the lap of his soon-to-be-appointed successor. Still,

when the new man came into office, he too tried to drop the case, since the court's own psychiatrists would support the contention of defense in regard to the defendant's mental competence at the time of the crime. Washington still "knew better" than its local U.S. Attorney, who now had no alternative but to go to court and take his lumps.

The trial lasted several days in which all the evidence was heard, including testimony from members of the plane's crew. Despite some difficulty with their conflicting testimony, it took the jury thirty minutes to acquit Sam.

Needless to say, Washington had a fit. They had no way to "get at" all the physicians, but they had one way to get at me. The Prosecution Division contacted the "right person" in the Bureau of Prisons, who in turn contacted the "right person" at the hospital for a "hush-hush" conference. The practical outcome of these shenanigans was that as of that date *I was to be allowed to see no more skyjackers in the routine course of my consultancy, but this new arrangement was to be concealed from me. In fact, if a skyjacker even came to the prison, that too was to be kept from me.*

Needless to say, within twenty-four hours I received one telephone call from Washington and three from a facility, each caller telling me just how the dice were being loaded.

At first, although miffed a little, I decided to overlook the matter and simply wait until skyjackers had been tried, and if they were convicted, study them in prison as I had done in many other cases.

With time out for some more reflection and plotting, Washington came up with a stunning new ploy: "He has found an organic basis upon which to base a legal defense; hence we must be sure he does not even see those already convicted, because this would give them a basis for appeal." Nothing could have been further from the truth, since we had stated from the beginning that such unusual organic aspects as could be found in these cases, could also be found among other categories of criminals.

Thus, studies of convicted prisoners came to a halt also. This was not actually very important from one point of view, for little new was emerging by that time (March, 1970). But from another point of view it was most damaging. There were various tests that ought to have been conducted in order to expand the studies, but no prison facility was adequately equipped for such tests, which would have required the use of medical school facilities and the assistance of the Federal Aviation Agency. Now, all such plans went down the drain.

I always presumed in the past that all of us, including the Department of Justice, were interested both in "justice" and in "good medicine." At this point, however, it became evident that the Department was interested in neither, but dedicated wholly to the principle of prosecution. Consequently, I stopped working with them and have acted by my own lights since.

The preceding problems with the Justice Department occurred many months after Sam was interviewed and did not occur in time to prevent me from seeing a number of other cases, which follow in this narrative.

A period of intense struggle developed at this juncture. Senators, presidential assistants, prominent colleagues, all threw their weight in. Then the truth emerged. There was no objection to this particular study. *All* study was forbidden. *The government would not allow investigation, even by its own departments.* The reason for this did not involve the explanation given in public, to the effect that the "constitutional rights of the men might be jeopardized." Quite the opposite, unless it is a constitutional right to be convicted. The real reason, not given publicly, was the fear that "any information uncovered by investigation might be subpoenaed by the defense."

The Congress had elected to control this matter by means of punishment and, regardless of what might make good sense, that was what was expected of the Department of Justice.

Fortunately, an unusually brilliant and kind man, and a former law partner of the President's, pointed out to me it was no great loss not to have the active support of the government in the project. To do so would only taint the study in the minds of other nations. They would suspect its contents, and thereby destroy any usefulness the study might have, as a basis for negotiation.

# IX

## Two More Cases

### THE CASE OF TED

Ted was forty-six, convicted for skyjacking in 1961. He came from an intact family with only one other child, a sister three and one-half years younger. He is divorced from his wife. They had four children, the oldest of whom accompanied him in his skyjacking.

Ted's father was a construction worker who brought in a steady income "until he started drinking, and of course, nobody who drinks heavy is really steady. He drank some when I was a child, but it was only for a short period of time as I recall. He got really hung up on booze after I got married. He became quite an alcoholic over a period of five or six years." Between the early alcoholic period and the later one, he became a church deacon at his wife's strong insistence. Ted and his father always had a close relationship, which was being maintained during his prison term.

The mother was a devout Baptist. Ted said she was "very Baptist. I think religion has had a very definite influence on my mother." He reported that he and his sister attended Sunday School "on a regular basis. The whole family went together, and it was Sunday School and church and BYPU and the whole bit." He often had to take care of his little sister.

Ted had an exceptional memory. "I can remember the first day I walked. I remember I was on the floor and I crawled up to a chair or something and pulled myself up. I remember my mother was in the next room; I think it was the kitchen, but I'm not positive. But I remember seeing her in the other room there and I

117

remember I pulled myself up to my feet, and I attempted to walk. I felt pretty good about it."

His only recollection of repetitive dreams from childhood was of "a prehistoric setting—a mammal-type creature like a slug came up out of the water and caught several people, but it didn't catch me. I woke up." From this dream he went on to say that he was sure he also often dreamed of falling. On inquiry, he stated he was *sure* he had never dreamed of flying.

During the first several years of school, he was a "straight A student. I think my grades definitely started deteriorating when I got into about the fifth grade. I wasn't interested for one thing, because it was becoming repetitious. I do remember something we were studying, I lost interest." He dropped out of school at the beginning of the ninth grade. At about the same time his grades in school declined, something interesting happened and the two are probably connected. "I enjoyed art from the first grade to the fourth. Then they told me that an artist is a sissy. I got that impression and it stuck with me for years." He didn't resume painting until he was in prison. His work now sells widely and an art dealer is considering him for a major show.

Ted reported having spent a great deal of time riding his bicycle. "That was my wheels as a kid, as we say today. Took me everywhere I went, practically. I've rode paper routes that were twenty-eight miles long." He learned to drive a car at about age fourteen and owned one at age sixteen.

He discovered sex at age five or six. "A little girl introduced me to the subject. I think she was two or three years older than me. As I recall, the first time she brought the subject up it was just a matter of how little kids happened to look, you know. Later she tried to have sexual relations." This experience aroused his curiosity, and he experimented with other girls. The girls were older and they were also the aggressors. "There were two or three of these girls, but this continued over a considerable period of time. I was between five and six years old and it continued until they were about eleven years old." He started dating when he was sixteen. He developed his first serious crush when he was seventeen.

He was engaged for two years. Then while he was in the Army, she married someone else and wrote him a "Dear John" letter.

He joined the National Guard at eighteen and was in the inactive reserve for about four months. He never went active because shortly after receiving the "Dear John" letter, he became so disturbed that he went AWOL. While he and a buddy were AWOL, they hitchhiked. "We caught a ride with this young fellow driving a Chevrolet, but his actions indicated that he was on the run from the law. He had also indicated that he might be armed. So what happened is, I slugged him with the intention of knocking him out and taking him to jail. It was pretty phony, you know—when a man was obviously trying to stay away from the cops. I just stunned him. So, anyhow, after calling the doctor and everything, why, I let him off at the hospital and told him the doctor had told me that he'd be right there and take care of him. And me and my partner left with the car . . . see? We didn't have any idea that we'd be involved in some kind of criminal activity with the automobile. The cops didn't catch us; we turned ourselves in to the Army." He pleaded guilty on the basis of a deal with the District Attorney for a suspended sentence, but was convicted and sentenced to fifteen months. He served five months before he was paroled.

Shortly afterward, his old girlfriend turned to him while trying to get away from her husband. "I was still very much in love with this girl myself, and from all indications she was still in love with me. She propositioned me to help her get a divorce and I went so far as to take her to talk to an attorney. But her husband, of course, I don't think he wanted to give her up at all, and I know that as a matter of fact he attempted to find me a couple of times when he was armed. I wasn't carrying a gun, but I had one available if I needed it. But it did look like things could get out of hand and develop into something real serious. And frankly, I just said to hell with it. And I didn't want to hurt the girl or see her get hurt. So I decided to pass a few checks and go back to prison. And that's exactly what I did." He was in prison on the forgery charge for sixteen months.

When he was twenty-one years old, he took flying lessons and qualified to fly a light plane. This was in 1945, and it took him only seven hours to fly solo. He flew only eleven or twelve hours in all because he could not afford it.

He married when he was twenty-one, after a two-week courtship. Their first child was born the first year. "I looked forward to it, I thought it was going to be a pretty fine thing to be a daddy." The first child was a son, closely followed by another, then by a daughter. Several years later, they had another son. Neither Ted nor his wife smoked or drank.

Prior to his marriage he had been working with his father in construction. Afterward, he became a truck driver. "We were kind of nomadic. We didn't stay too long in one place. Working conditions had something to do with it, and we wasn't in any great big hurry to settle down. We didn't want any roots. We were just happy-go-lucky. We didn't take life too damned serious, but we tried to enjoy ourself." He and his wife moved to three different states, staying briefly at several places in each. He quit the trucking business and became a miner. "In 1949, I went to work for a power company, and I stayed with them nine whole months before I quit." This was the longest time he held a job, except for one that he held for a little over a year in 1954.

After this long tenure, he had some money saved and he was not working, so he decided to have himself committed to a mental hospital to see whether conditions there were as bad as people said they were. "I went to a certain amount of trouble to try to prepare myself to gain entrance. I have been an avid reader of the literature, publications, weeklies, monthlies, and so forth. The best I could come up with was to try to convince people that I was a little bit despondent. It seemed to me like an opportune time to satisfy my curiosity, so I did." He was in the hospital for about twenty-eight days.

He went into selling. In 1957, he moved and worked for a transportation company as a service man. While he was employed there, his cousin robbed the company. It looked like an inside job, and Ted was arrested. "I didn't commit the crime, and I didn't execute it, and I didn't plan it. But I done time for it." He was in prison thirty-three months. "But these things don't happen in the United States, do they?" The Castro revolution occurred while he was in prison, and the patient watched it closely. He decided "while I was in prison, that I was going to leave the United States [because of his false imprisonment]. I hadn't determined at that time that it was necessarily going to be to Cuba."

When he came out of prison, he began selling cars. He found that while he was in prison, his wife "became quite involved in religious matters and church activities and so forth. I didn't object to her going to church and taking the kids to church. I've never done that. I don't think anybody can appreciate freedom more than someone who has been denied freedom. She told me that she wanted to become a missionary. I quoted some Scripture at her that this wasn't the way it was supposed to be done. A woman wasn't supposed to—and her husband, either, for that matter— wasn't supposed to split up the home and his family for such a ridiculous thing as that."

He further explained that his wife was religious, but lax on discipline. "There's something else that happened during this period of confinement that caused me to feel and resent this thing more than just the fact that I was not guilty of the damn crime to begin with. It was the fact that the children were going away from me. There was no discipline." When he tried to establish order in the household, the children considered him a "big dictator." "That caused my resentment against the authorities to increase a lot. Even today, I hate the state with a passion. It's safe to say that I hate what they represent, law and justice. But I found in the last few months that I was locked up in prison, I could tell from the kids' manner of speech, little things, they showed disrespect, you know."

Soon after his release from prison, Ted went to Mexico City. He went to the Cuban Consulate there, and inquired about the school system, living conditions, and the possibility of going to Cuba. "I applied for citizenship and told them I wanted to request political asylum. I was granted residence." He took the whole family down to Mexico, with their consent, and made plans to go to

Cuba. Before he could leave, however, he had to return to the States to finish some paper work on his car sales. He planned to return shortly and then leave for Cuba. He believes that while he was gone his wife wrote the authorities and claimed he was trying to force the family to go to Cuba. He had broken parole by leaving the state, and before he could return to Mexico, "I get a call from the parole officer, telling me to remain there at my father's house and wait for my parole officer. He gets there about two hours later and he tells me that the state is screaming for my arrest. He informed me that it might be a good thing if I'd hire an attorney. I told him, I said, I hadn't broken any laws. I hadn't committed any crimes. I didn't say that I hadn't broken my parole. He said, 'I thought maybe that you and your partner had been selling some hot cars in Mexico.' I said, 'The FBI is barking up the wrong tree if they're looking for something there.'"

He then received a letter from his wife saying the family was returning from Mexico and had decided not to go to Cuba. "So I tell 'em that they can either go back or whatever they damn well please, that I was still wanting to go to Cuba, because that's just the way it is. The Cuban government had given us citizenship, not only me, but my entire family, and that as soon as we decided we want to go to Cuba, the Cuban government would pay air transportation all the way for my entire family." At this point, his family deserted him and he expected the federal authorities to arrest him. "I didn't think I had any choice at the time." He skyjacked. "They had me in a place where I was crawling. I either had to do what I did, or I had to split altogether, leave my family, and head for Mexico. I was pretty sure when I boarded the aircraft that I wouldn't go any farther than El Paso. 'Cause they could do what they damned well pleased, but I done some research while I was being researched and it's a well-known fact that these airlines, at that time for economy reasons, were fueling at these intermediate stops. I knew this, I knew the plane would never make it to Cuba without refueling."

He had his oldest son with him. He was sixteen years old at the time and went with his father because he wanted to. "Nobody forced him. My other oldest boy wanted to go and I wouldn't take him. I wouldn't have taken the oldest if it hadn't been for his mother and sister. They both, all the time during the year before I was released on parole, why, they couldn't get along, always fighting." The son told the authorities later that they were stealing the aircraft and were going to sell it in Cuba. Ted was perplexed over this. "It'd be pretty damned ridiculous. It belongs to the air-line." The son was held in juvenile authority for a while, then released. He has not contacted his father since he entered prison.

## General Comments

This case is important insofar as it provides clinical material dating back to the beginning of American skyjacking (1961).

It was assuring to find the familiar family constellation, and exciting to encounter the first memory of walking, particularly when the symbolism of body posture came through in Ted's feeling that he had been forced into a position where he "had to crawl." When this comment was followed by the statement, "Once a man has learned to stand, and have dignity, you can't take it away from him," I almost embedded my old tape recorder in plaster to preserve the phraseology.

It is also interesting to note that, at about the same age as Will (whose case history follows Ted's), Ted was very interested in art. Both were dissuaded from their interest by older males who suggested that art was for homosexuals. Note that both men later became involved in forgery. In his own mind, Will elevated forgery to the level of an "art" in which he could compare himself with the masters of the past.

Another interesting aspect of this case is the familiar exaggerated lateral movement required by his job as a young man, and also in his brief participation in flying. Of special interest in this respect is Ted's general physical condition. He is in the best emotional shape of all the prisoners we have seen, although he has been imprisoned the longest. He feels that an important cause of his condition is that he walks or jogs a considerable distance every day in the prison exercise yard.

## THE CASE OF WILL

Will came from a middle-class family in the Midwest. He was the youngest of five children, two of his siblings being brothers, and two sisters, in that order of birth. Will was thirty-one years old at the time of our interview.

The father was a salesman who earned a steady income. He was exceedingly authoritative over his wife and the other children, but more lenient to Will, perhaps because he was the youngest. "He was very strict with my brothers and sisters; then I came along and he was getting older. He became more—he eased up a little. When I say strict, I don't necessarily mean punishment; he always made them work. My brothers always had work, and he wouldn't put up with any back talk or arguing."

The mother was submissive to her husband. "She listened to my father. She was pretty well a slave for him." The patient reluctantly admitted that he was the favorite child. "I don't think that I deserved to be his favorite. He sort of put the favoritism where it shouldn't have belonged. I haven't lived up to it, no, and I made so many mistakes."

The father was Catholic, the mother Presbyterian. Will incorporated some of both traditions into his personal religious beliefs. Sometimes as a child he felt "pulled between them in this regard." He believed in Heaven and Hell. "I think Hell would be a burning of the soul and Heaven would be a satisfying of one's soul. I believe Heaven's within, and Hell's probably without." He further described Heaven as "peace of mind." Desire would be gone in Heaven. "It would be gone because it would be fair, and I imagine all the things you hoped for would be right there."

As far back as he can remember, Will has been having dreams about falling and paralysis. "You fall off a cliff or something, and you wake up. I've had a dream before that where I tried to get enough strength, or I couldn't make my legs run fast enough. Heavy, heavy, it would just feel like I couldn't. I didn't have enough strength." He also frequently had dreams of flying. "I'd start to run and I'd have to leap up in the air. It was like swimming.

I'd have to make my arms go like this [makes swimming motions]. I'd make a long leap and then I'd come down. Each leap would be maybe a little longer. I'd start going up, but there again I'd have to fight pretty hard to get up in the air. I mean I'd have to make my arms move pretty well. But then, one time I got up too high and I got scared, so I came down. This dream is better, better to get away from something. The feeling of getting away, being loose from, nothing can hold you down." He reported having had similar feelings in airplanes. "Leaving everything, it's like a new beginning, like starting, like leaving things behind."

His earliest memory was of riding his tricycle around the block by himself at about age six, "Kind of scared, wondering if I'd get back." He recalled his mother's taking him to school the first day. He enjoyed first grade, but in the second grade, he rebelled. His first act of rebellion was in art class. "My brother said that only sissies stay inside the lines so I scribbled instead of staying inside the lines. I didn't try to do the work." He started truancy in the fifth grade. He rarely participated in sports. "We had a tree house, and we stayed up there and smoked pipes."

He recalled only three friends. His peers had no nickname for him and he was then and continued to be unconcerned about having friends. He was "kicked out of school" in the tenth grade. He was touchy about this and preferred to say that he quit school. "About the same time, they expelled me and I went back and told them 'I quit anyway.' I wasn't there half the time."

He had his first date when he was thirteen. He was first intimate with a girl at seventeen. In both instances the girls took the initiative. From seventeen on, he dated occasionally, but never went steady.

Will had vague memories of stealing small items, such as golf balls, as early as age seven. He clearly remembered stealing in early adolescence. "I used to go into a grocery store and pick up cases of empty bottles and Coca-Cola bottles, take them up and get the deposit on them. I did that about twelve, eleven or twelve. One time I can remember back, thirteen years old, around Christmas time, I was selling Christmas cards and collecting all the money and keeping it. I progressed, the more I learned. I'd try everything. I went into checks and forgeries more than anything." Forgery began in connection with report cards, at about the seventh grade. "Actually, what I did was, I'd bring one and forget that and tell them I lost it. Then I'd get another one, so I'd have two report cards, one to show my parents and the other one."

At age seventeen, he joined the Coast Guard. He was in service for a month. "I guess I just didn't like it, the discipline and the regimentation. You wasn't to know the honest answers. I felt superior in myself and I was wasting my time in there. I could get out and travel around the country, but I didn't want to go AWOL. So I figured I was smart enough to talk my way out of it. I'd get up and I'd stencil my hat on the outside. I'd always fold things and unfold them, things that I had heard and read that people did who were a little off-balance." He received a discharge from the Coast Guard.

Will was very proud of his forging abilities. "I can take things out of a signature that you have to look at with a microscope, do it so perfect that I had a hard time seeing where I had forged it myself. It became pride. Why should I work at some job or be in the Coast Guard, or be in school for that matter, when I can go out and use my talent? I have enough ability to do this, to forge right now without having years and years of creating some other kind of honest work. I wanted it right away. I didn't want to wait." Speaking of technique, he explained, "The first thing I'd do, I work on carbon copies, I use a stylus, and I use all-purpose pencil erasers." During the interview, he quickly produced a quite credible copy of the interviewer's signature.

He had an interesting technique which he used successfully for five years across the country. "I'd call for reservations. I wouldn't tell them I was staying one night. I'd tell them I'd be there about ten days, ten or twelve, that I was at the airport and I'd be in as soon as I could call a taxi." Actually, he might be calling from next door, but he wanted to create the image of an important person. "Then I'd set myself up either in a hotel or some apartment. I'd tell them I worked for some big company. I'd pick a name that didn't exist, but sounded like the name of a famous company. I'd tell them that I was just located in the area, and I had some figuring to do or something like that, like I was an advertising salesman. That's the first thing I'd do, and then I'd get the phone book and see where the places were that I could make some money—department stores—I'd hit them with a check or I'd buy something and then I'd take it back." The purpose of the elaborate pretense at the hotel was to establish identification for the check. "They'd want to know who I was, where I was located. I'd tell the hotel. Usually I'd have them deliver it right to the hotel. I'd take them back to another store. I'd make an average of two to three hundred a day." He divided the country into sections and systematically worked each. He estimated that he traveled about twenty thousand miles a year. Most of the time he traveled and worked alone.

During this period, he spent a lot of money on women. Often it was for prostitutes, but a great deal went toward impressing women with his importance. "I told one I was Walter Dupont, Jr. She believed it for about a day. She was looking for someone with money, so I told her that. Depends on what they're looking for, what I tell them. Tell them whatever they want to hear . . . either a name that's familiar with someone [or] a name that sounds like wealth's attached to it." He admitted to being impressed with his own act.

After five years of success he was caught, and spent the following years in and out of jail. He was remorseful about this. "I look at these things and they're painful. I wish I could go back and do them over again. Wish I could go back to school. If I had it to do over again, I'd do it different. I'd study in school. I wouldn't waste as much time as I've wasted in thievery and things and have ended in nothing. If I could have, if I had a different attitude, I could have made something of myself."

Will expressed some of these feelings to his father the last time he saw him. He was in prison at the time. "I promised him when I got out and everything, I'd settle down. Things would be all right. That was the last time I'd be in trouble." He was very disturbed by his father's death. "I cried. It tore me up. I didn't know that he was going. I knew that he was ill, but I didn't know that it was cancer. Took me a little time to get over it."

During this prison term, Will decided the best way to get out quickly was to pretend insanity as he had done while in the Coast Guard. "First I went up on the water tower and I stood there and *I told them I was going to fly.* I had to look for a pattern. After I got down I had to draw things that could fly, that in reality couldn't—boats and a horse and maybe a knight on a horse, put long eye-lashes on the horse, little things. I felt that I definitely could feel what they were looking for, the pattern they were looking for, so I drew a character on a horse with a mustache on him and let my mustache grow. That was supposed to mean that I identified myself with the character on the horse."

Will had very strong patriotic convictions. He believed that sky-jackers ought to be shot. "They're like treason. They're trying to forget their country. They're un-American. I can't understand why anybody would want to go, want to think about it."

As to the skyjacking attempt, five years later Will admitted only that he was charged with air piracy. He had finished his jail sentence and was through with parole when a new set of charges were brought against him and he was arrested. His dreams about paralysis returned. He was being taken by two detectives on a commercial airline to stand trial. "That was the end. I'd just gotten out, I didn't want to go back. I would have done anything not to go back. They said they were going to turn this over to the FBI, and everything, and to the federals, hell when they said it, I knew that was it." He was supposed to have passed a note to a stewardess threatening the aircraft. "There was a note. I guess they have it. That's the whole thing, I don't know whether they have the note or not. That's a conviction, right there, the note."

Will was desperate. "I made up my mind. I didn't want to go back, period. I might have done something that might have led to being killed, maybe running, something like that." He admitted that he would not have cared if they had shot him, and that he had been feeling that way since his father's death. "Rather than spend my life in jail, I'd rather be sent before a firing squad. Gas chamber would do just as well. Then you don't have the guilt on you, taking your own life. I feel that taking your own life is admitting defeat to everything. Condemn you to take your own life."

## General Comments

Most of the material in this case is familiar by now. What is exceptionally vivid here is the suicidal "now or never" aspect. Unlike other skyjackers who assume that they have the only gun on the plane, Will not only had none, but knew for sure that at least two armed detectives were aboard with him. This type of behavior pattern is more or less apparent in a number of others who, like many bank robbers, carry unloaded guns that will "draw fire," but that cannot fire back. The late Willie Sutton used to carry a "gun" carved out of a bar of soap and coated with shoe polish. This potentially suicidal intent, whereby one wants to "die like a man," is a trait shared by skyjackers and bank robbers.

Particularly interesting was the fact that in this interview the patient wore a full-length plaster cast on his leg. He had broken his leg in an attempted jail break when he jumped from a third-story window. When asked if he thought he could fly, he retorted, "What's the matter, do you think I'm crazy?"

# X

# A Duet:
# A Skyjacking by Lovers

## GLADYS

Gladys was the only female in our sample, and one of the very few women who have been involved in skyjacking; she was nineteen years old.

Her childhood was marred by her parents' unhappy home life, attributed primarily to the father's drinking and to sexual incompatibility. They separated when Gladys was thirteen years old, and her brother—her only sibling—was fifteen.

At one time, the father was one-fourth owner of a business that collapsed; he was unable to hold on to steady employment after that. He was graduated at a distinguished university, but he was a chronic alcoholic who became quite abusive when drunk. "He threw things around, but he never hit anybody. Yeah, he hit me, but he never hit my mother. For example, he would just throw things around and break things and stamp around."

He was particularly violent with her brother. "My father used to abuse him, wow! Well, he's very sick. He had a lot of hang-ups and he couldn't stand the thought of having another man in the house other than himself. So, as my brother matured, especially when he got to be in his teens, my father practically freaked out. He would pick a fight with him over anything, you know, anything at all. He would shout at him and rant and rave." The brother is now twenty-one years old and a serious student. "He's a very tense person, stutters, you know, he's really tense."

130

According to Gladys, a meaningful father-son relationship never existed. She believed that her brother resented her closeness to their father when she was young, although she and her brother were very close and loving until she was five, when her father "took her over." She said the brother used to "smother me, strangle me, and we would come home from school and have lunch together. My mother and father weren't there, and he used to try to scare me and he'd say he wasn't really my brother. He'd get a knife[1] (laughter) and he'd say, 'You think I'm your brother, I'm not really your brother,' and all this other trash." The knife threats, she felt, were directed at his resentment of her closeness to the father.

The mother had a master's degree in music, and gave private lessons for fifteen years until her separation from her husband. Afterward, she taught school. Both children studied music. She had been seeing a psychiatrist; she was always emotionally unstable. "She'd wander around the streets and policemen asked her where she lived and stuff. She'd wear baggy clothes. She was out of it. She was sick and marrying my father was a mistake."

The father was Catholic and the mother Unitarian, but neither was actively religious. Gladys was baptized as a Catholic, but never confirmed; only recently did she attend her first mass.

From about her fourth year, the father has had an incestuous relationship with her. "My recollection is always—I know it must sound weird, but as long as I can remember my father always took naps with me, took showers with me [laugh], he was really weird, and you know, I thought this was normal, natural. Then I started going to school and something of the secrecy of it communicated itself to me and I began to realize. . . ." The relationship apparently fell short of intercourse, but they masturbated each other and had other erotic sex play. As a young child, she was pleased to keep "our secret" and believed it to be normal. Later, when she began to suspect abnormality, she became emotionally upset and avoided her peers.

She was unable to discuss the situation with her mother for many

---

[1] The knife had been given to her parents as a wedding gift.

years. The father claimed that the mother must have known about it, but the mother admitted only to vague suspicions of something amiss. The father referred to himself as a "perverse being who should never have married." Gladys finally confided in her mother at age thirteen, and it seemed to have contributed to the separation of the parents. Their status was that of legal separation, and the father rarely paid the obligatory monthly child support payments.

Gladys always resented school. "Kindergarten stank." She explained: "They want you completely, but all they can have is your body, and the same thing in prison, right? They've got you in the classroom $x$ number of hours every day. However, when you're looking out the window, you're not necessarily with them, which is a source of frustration with them, especially young children, good heavens, you can hardly get their attention." Speaking of elementary school: "I consider I never learned anything in school. As far as knowledge is concerned, because, hum, as it got later and later, it became more and more of a farce. Okay, you can teach somebody to read and write. That's teaching him something, but all this other crap they put on you, there's no need, there's no need for twelve years in school even. You can learn to read and write in two or three years, then let them go to the library." She said she discovered their "game": "Fold your hands, be quiet, do the test. You know, don't deviate. If you're different, keep your mouth shut and nobody will notice." She further explained her resentment by saying, "Okay, why do you go to school? Learn to read and write? Come off it. To prepare yourself for society. Now, society has a particular sickness, right? If you want to fit in, you got to be their kind of sick. Okay, I can't be. I got to be my kind of sick, so they tried to teach me to be their kind of sick. I went to school. They pumped all this deadly blah, blah, all over me. I just didn't catch on to it."

She reported making her first friend in the fourth grade. She had few friends and preferred to be alone. She often wore four or five dresses to school, one over the other. She wondered if it might have been her way of always being ready to run away.

Asked about dreams, she readily reported recurring dreams of flying. "I'm flying, I'm able to fly, and I'm flying and flying and flying—just me, flying. There are people tangled up in telephone wires, and I can't go before I let them through. Before I let them free, I have to free them, you know, they're all tangled up, so I free them and there are hundreds of people, big chore. And then, I see a whole crowd of people who look exactly like my mother standing on the ground, and they're facing up to me. I say, 'Who's my mother?' and they all say, 'I am.' Every single one of them. And I say, 'Wow!' So, I'm flying through them and there's a whole bunch of people, and every single one of them looks like my brother. I say, 'Who's my brother?', and they all say, 'I am.' And I'm flying and I see a whole crowd of people who look exactly like my father and I say, 'Who's my father?', and they all say, 'I am.' So I go back home and I go into the kitchen and there's just three witches with pointed hats and black costumes, no brooms, in my kitchen. I never saw those witches fly. My witches never fly. I used to have a kind of masochistic fantasy with my witches during the day— they did some of the wildest things to people, me included (laughter). They would pounce on me, put me in a typewriter, and type on me. They would make a lampshade out of me. They would use me for a mattress, me and others. Oh, they were wild, they were the wildest witches. I had the witches for the longest time, until, maybe, I don't know, maybe twelve or so —I felt mostly flat most of the time, they used you for rugs and stuff. And you were like, I guess they used you for a piece of paper or something. These witches—and they all have those hats."

She also reported dreams of heaviness, "Like being chased on the school grounds by a big monster and not being able to get up in the air, but you know you can fly [laughter], but you can't get started—frustration—paralyzed." She had these dreams frequently until she was about fifteen years old.

She described herself as "anti-gravity, very." She enjoyed the leaps in ballet lessons because they got her off the ground. "Wow, that is what you want, to fill yourself up with air and the sensation of flying is such a thing I was after. I'd jump and try to defy it—to stay in the air. Just to try to keep on jumping. To me, that major feeling was the freeness, the freeness of it. Try to get free."

The patient's first intercourse was rape, on her way to school one morning at age thirteen. After that, she had several affairs. "I know this is corny, but I really wanted somebody to love me, you know? I really did. These guys—I can't, you know—who is to blame in these situations? They, some of them might have tried to reach me, I don't know, but, at any rate, we never communicated. We would just sleep around together and I just—we'd go to school, and I don't know, I was taking some drugs. . . ." She developed deep guilt feelings from sexual activities until she met George.

When she was fifteen, she made a suicide attempt. She explained that she was "tired. And cosmic, you know, the cosmic sadness that strikes humans. Well, I just wore it. I was sick, sick, sick—unreality. I'd look at the trees and they were painted, and the sky was a backdrop and the people—I don't know what they were. So what was the point?" She took some benzedrine, a half bottle of aspirin, and some of her mother's sleeping pills. "I was taking them with wine punch and I ran out of the wine punch. I didn't want to take them with water because we don't have cold water at home—kind of blah, so I started taking them with milk. I was really getting nauseous. I was afraid I was going to throw up and blow the whole thing, and I kept taking these pills and these pills, oh!" She was found in a comatose state by her mother and rushed to the hospital. She was in a coma for thirty hours. Afterward, she remained in the psychiatric ward for two months.

She met George the summer she turned seventeen. He was living with another girl, who was a friend of Gladys'. "He was leaning against the fence, oh, wow! He had a suede jacket on, that's right, and a white shirt, and blue jeans, and he was just leaning there, *waiting*. And I walked out and he saw me and he was still waiting because he wasn't really waiting for me, he was waiting for something else." In ecstatic terms, she described their relationship after she had ousted her friend: "We'd do everything together, and we'd get so silly, we'd laugh for hours over nothing. We'd play these silly word games. We did everything, man, pillow fight, run around, play baseball. Oh, wow! He's so beautiful. Wow, when I make love to him—when I made love to all those other guys, I turned myself off, but with him, oh! It's so different! It's like a whole new thing."

Although Gladys was living at home with her mother at the time, George moved in with her. The mother explained that she had been disturbed over Gladys' promiscuity and was relieved to have her confine her attention to one love object. She neither encouraged nor discouraged the relationship.

She denied having used mind-expanding drugs, except LSD on two occasions—both times with George. On one acid trip, two months before the crime, she experienced a feeling of flight. "We got to the top of the hill and I said, 'Can we actually fly now, can we actually jump off this world?' and he said, 'Sure, we can,' so we kind of jumped off the world, you know." She took LSD because George was doing it and she wanted to be with him. "I'd say, 'Well, if you're high and I'm not, how can this work?' So we took acid together."

She was hostile toward the space program. "Okay, here are these fools, trying to fuck the universe, right? With their little rocket. Right? Infinity goes both ways. Naturally it goes out, but it also goes in, into yourself, past, past everything."

She claimed that she would be able to kill for George, but she did not realize this until their arrest. She stated that if something happened to him while he was in prison, "I would kill for him, and if there's anything wrong with him, if they've done anything that love won't cure, I'm going to get some of them before they get me. I'd go to the police station and shoot the policeman and I'd shoot— I'd just massacre."

She didn't have negative political feelings about the United States. "I am apolitical and George is a radical, but I have always been apolitical, just simply, it's just a whole other thing that I don't even —I can't even groove it, any of it. See, it's the way I feel." She did not particularly want to go to Cuba, but felt "there doesn't seem to be any place for us, there really doesn't." She felt the skyjacking was necessary for the sake of George's "manhood," not for the sake of going to Cuba. "You see, to me it was like the coming of manhood for him. *The first stand-up* and like, all the other time he was hiding."

She loved the flight itself. "There was the elation, yes. It was the seas and the water. It was beautiful. It was a beautiful flight—and I felt elated." She also expressed a desire to skydive. She adored the rides at fairs. "Now you're rocking back and forth, way on the edge, and this thing is right here and you're holding on to it and you're looking down. The thing about the roller coaster is the falling. You don't zoom up, you crawl up and then you zoom down, and you're crawling up and you want to go up. You want the thing to go even higher, you know, like you're leaning forward and everything is kind of behind you and there's just a moment, you know, and you get to and you can see the whole fair if you're looking, but you're not because you're on the very, very top."

She often felt separated from her body. She saw her body as "meaningless, sad." She said she felt "above" her body. "I'm a mind, and I'm lonely, sad, lonesome, a sadness in my throat, but I'm not even aware of my body very much."

She retained definite suicidal tendencies. She had an urge to jump from balconies whenever she was on one. She said that she would enjoy dying by jumping out of a plane. Death to her was a redirection of the energy of life. "You can't destroy energy, it just changes, so you change, and maybe clouds are the souls of people who die. I would like to fly straight out into the arms of the stars, into the night and feel myself thinner and thinner, like cigarette smoke, until I was the stars in the night, you know, so maybe I was just like one of them."

Her overall attitude toward George was worshipful. "I intend to kneel down and kiss his feet—because he is beautiful and he is good and he is so brave, and I would like to heap gifts on him, I would like to shower him with things. Religion is that I love you."

Her attitude toward the skyjacking was: "It was a very desperate thing—if we got caught, well, we'd just die." She wondered whether prison might not be purgatory. "It's not fair, somebody writes a check and gets sent off for three years. Now, did the man in charge of the bank suffer? Who suffered? What is money? Paper. This person, though, this person is getting part of his life taken away, confiscated, but it's not tangible, it's not tangible those days you take away from them. I wanted to cry out [to the judge], 'You suffer, but you won't admit it and you don't know it, so why are we trying to hurt each other? Why are you trying me? You've been hurt. Don't you know, don't you feel it?' You're trapped [meaning herself in prison], sure, but you know it. These people only suspect it. And, shit, they're fifty years old, they're retired. Their life is gone, gone, and where did it ever go? If they started thinking, where did it ever go?"

## GEORGE

George was white, twenty-one years old, highly intelligent. He came from an intact Catholic family. He had a half sister, four years older, who was born to his mother's previous marriage.

George gave many examples of an unhappy home situation and much marital strife. The father worked as a clerk. He was dissatisfied with his position, especially since he was getting older and saw no prospect of being promoted to the executive level. He was a heavy drinker and very abusive when drunk. He was the type of man who could "beat any girl on the block," but was subdued in the presence of other men. George described his father's "prowling about the house, banging doors, knocking the refrigerator to the floor. He didn't do anything physical to either my sister or myself, but he would attack objects that represented my sister. He would go into her closet and tear up all her clothes and things like that."

There was perpetual warfare between the father and the mother, including a struggle for the love of the children. "He tried to tell me about the, you know, 'males against the females.' My mother sided with my sister. He was the 'only one looking out for me.' That was the hardest thing. But, you know, I didn't think my mother deserved. . . ." He ended up siding with his mother.

The mother preferred the sister to George. Although this required that he accept a secondary role, he seems to have concealed his resentment. As a group, they excluded the father.

George recalled being sexually involved with a girl for about a year when he was six, and the girl eight or nine. He remembered her being the aggressor in the relationship. He recalled playing spacemen and cowboys and Indians with her. He could not recall the exact nature of the sexual relationship, but he felt that it was there.

He had an active fantasy interest in athletics all his life. One of his early memories was a pantomime. "I'd get a stick and a crumpled cup and throw it into the air. I used to be a Dodger fan and I used to know all the batting averages of all the different players. I'd be there all day long, playing games against the Yankees. Actually, I was acting out all these different parts; Jim Gilliam got up first, Peewee Reese got up second, Duke Snyder got up third; I knew all their different ways of batting, and I knew some were right-handed and some were left-handed. I'd hit a fly ball to center and ole Mickey Mantle's out there and he's pretty fast and he probably could have got it and you're out, and all that kind of stuff." This continued until he was fourteen or fifteen years old. He engaged in some sports activities with neighborhood children and at school, but he was not very skillful.

One of his earliest and most frequent dreams was of floating. "Generally a very 'up' feeling, drifting over landscapes. For some reason, there's always a corner block. I think I pretty much drifted around, wasn't in control of my own motions. I remember it was very exciting. *Totally different from how I felt when I was awake.* It was a whole different experience. My whole body felt different. It wasn't rooted on the ground, I didn't relate the dream to real life, but when I was dreaming I really felt how good it was." On numerous occasions in dreams, he was rooted to the ground by a great heaviness and was unable to "break free" of the pull. At such times, he made no effort physically to break free. He either floated spontaneously or awoke in fear. The heavy sensations he experienced when he was awake and in non-floating dreams have continued to the present time. He reported that he wet his bed until he was at least twelve years old.

He was an altar boy, chiefly at his mother's insistence, from the second grade through the first year of high school. He recalled feelings of awe concerning the altar: "Just a kind of strange, confused deep remoteness. You look at the tabernacle. You look right through it into a great void, where He was." He once believed in the Devil: "The Devil was, seems to be, more inside of you than outside of you. God and Heaven seem to be more outside than inside. It seems as if you're always trying to conquer the Devil inside you. It always gets to the outside, it wasn't the other way around. Like selfishness, it always seemed to be a Devil. When you're doing something that was selfish, your parents would holler at you or the monks would holler at you. They would say, 'That's the Devil.' The doctrine also says that the body is the temple of Christ and God's temple, but usually they emphasize the body's being taken over by the Devil more than they emphasize the fact that the body's God's temple. So they emphasize the Devil inside more than they emphasize the God inside." These religious concerns were intimately related to the "physical sensations of a heavy body, filled with lassitude, and a lightness of the head." These contradictions in doctrine, as well as his rebellion against the formalities, eventually caused him to quit attending church at age fifteen.

He described himself as a "nervous" first-grader. He rarely prepared an assignment, preferring to copy a girl's work before school. He received high marks during grade school, but remarked, "I don't think the nuns were very objective in the marking. It's mostly my fault, but partly their fault. I never learned anything in depth. It was always superficial, by-the-textbook type of thing."

He reported having an active temper that flared in the face of failure and disappointment. His nickname was "Pepper." By virtue of his friendship with the school leader, he had status among the other boys.

In high school, he experienced a drastic change of attitude. He flunked several courses and was switched to a public high school, from which he graduated. Describing his changed attitude, he said, "I don't know, I think I just suddenly realized that I was living in a competitive world and the things I'd been doing all along weren't going to be able to make me a fit living. I began to think about getting older and getting a job and things like that, and I began to look at what was happening around me. I felt very depressed thinking about it. I used to ask myself what I was going to do and how I was going to live, and I didn't have any answers. So I was in a spiral, circular reasoning, questions with no answers, around and around, and I'd just like to drop out of the whole thing. I just pushed the whole thing off the desk, off my mind. I'd go out and run around and play basketball and drink quantities of beer." His general feeling of lethargy became worse at this time. "I would come home from school and lie down and go to sleep until six o'clock, then get up and eat supper and go sit and watch television until ten o'clock, go upstairs and go to bed, and feel tired in the morning, skip school."

He admitted he had trouble with spatial concepts. He did not drive a car. "I don't feel any identification with a car. When I turn the wheel to back up, I always get confused." He disliked riding in a car with someone who was not driving "evenly." He also stated that circus rides that go around and around were very distressing to him.

His first serious girlfriend appeared when he was fifteen. There was no sex, just necking. She was the aggressor in the relationship. He described her as having the "sparkle" that he lacked. Following her, there was a brief episode with "this all-American, cheerleader, cream cheese," who also was the aggressor. The girl with whom he had intercourse for the first time had long black hair and brown eyes. "She came from the city and she had lived all over. She was kind of the forward-type activist, I guess. I was in love with her for about two years. She was a big bird." (Predator?) He was eighteen at this time. "My folks kind of knew about it, and they even talked about it. They got very, very upset and wanted me to break off with her and this kind of stuff. They really get you down. *Down* is sighs and 'Oh, my God' and 'What are we going to do?' and 'What's happening?' " He believed he made the initial sexual move, but that she had solicited him. Describing sex with her, he said, "I didn't feel much. Emotionally I didn't feel much. I think she liked more brutality than I could give her." His parents bought him a motorcycle as a bribe to break off with the "bird," but he soon used it to cover the distance between his house and hers. After his freshman year in college, he moved in with her. She had a small income, and he worked part-time.

He commented that he could see that he "used her as an escape action and as kind of forward scout for my life. She had gone on and set up a world of her own, separated from her parents. So I separated from my parents. She did all the ditrty work, but I just kind of stepped into it. I think that I don't spend much time putting up *my own thing,* but step into other people's things."

Gladys disrupted this relationship. His impression of their first meeting was, "Two creatures kind of saw each other and having seen each other, drew apart. Gladys was always appearing and disappearing. She's always mysterious. She'd appear at two o'clock in the morning and disappear. She'd not be there for a week, and she might not be there for a month. Then she'd appear and disappear. I first thought she was kind of a snotty type of person. She was always very distant and very cold." He and Gladys did no more than observe one another for a long while. "And then the bird and I began a long period of disenchantment. She began to get more and more dependent on me, and I was hardly a person to be dependent on. Stopped going to school, dropped out. She was always around, always wanting silverware. I thought it was impossible. She wanted to depend on me when I knew I was nothing to depend on. She liked *The New York Times* and all kinds of strange things, a lot of ritzy things. I wasn't particuarly that type of person. I finally drove her away from the nest. She left, and after a period of a month or two, Gladys began coming over to see me and things like that. Then one night we made love together, and after that we pretty much recognized."

George claimed that he was the aggressor in this relationship, "'Cause she was, she didn't want to, she seemed as if she was trying to draw away and I was trying to draw her to me. She was trying to fade away. She would get that look in her eyes. She would just kind of disappear sometimes." Describing sex with her, he said, "There was more electricity, an exchange of energies. Almost like exploding. The bird was kind of slop through the mud, quagmire, cloudy type of thing. That's the way it seemed. After a while, with Gladys I had to admit that *it was* because it kept happening. That it was real, didn't just happen, in some kind of strange, beautiful thing."

During his association with "the bird," he had begun using marijuana. After his relationship with Gladys began, they tried LSD together. "Making love was very, very beautiful. I remember she played music. We were very close then." Speaking of his love for her, he said, "It's hard to put into words. It's kind of like two pieces just fit together. I remember the feeling. It's difficult to remember the joy of every day."

Although Gladys was living with her mother, George moved in with her. "The mother made no objections, because she wanted Gladys to be happy. Her mother is a very unusual and very beautiful person." Again, he had moved *to* a woman. He felt guilty because some of his aimlessness and dissatisfaction with life rubbed off on Gladys. "She knew where she was going. She was going to dance until she got good. Then she was going to be a dancer somewhere or be a musician somewhere. She had those two things to kind of form a basis. I think I dissolved the dance relationship because I got jealous of it. So finally she stopped going to dance. Then she went to a music conservatory in September, and she couldn't stay there for I don't know what reasons. I like to think that she came back because of me. I don't know exactly, and I felt badly, very badly."

His feelings for Gladys had a great impact on his life. "I just want to be able to earn enough to keep her and myself living comfortable. I'd like to have her play music somewhere. I'd like for her to be able to be happy. And I can't make either one of those. I could be someone for her to love. I always get excited listening to her. The way she talks, it's like reading Tolstoy."

He was rootless and had no ambitions. "I was just going through the motions of what I was doing because I had no idea what else I could do. So I was going to school because I had always been going to school. So after I graduated, I didn't have any real interest in going on into a four-year school, and I just didn't really know what I was going to do. I was interested in photography, in writing, in people, and I was interested in Gladys. I couldn't seem to put them all together and come up with a form of life, a form of making a living. I knew I didn't want to be a teacher. I knew I didn't want to be a lot of things, but I didn't know what I wanted to be. I considered dropping all the way out, doing some kind of farm work, agricultural work, but I didn't have the gumption to do it because I had been living so soft all my life without working. It was difficult. I was chained by a lot of things, cigarettes, Pepsi-Cola. I didn't want to give those things up. So I was incapable of getting out of it, but I was incapable of staying in it. So I felt that if I made a *big jump* into a new situation, things would get better, because I had always had a lot of difficulty in making decisions, making changes."

He believed that being white and living in the North made him unfairly privileged. Dreaming of Cuba, the two of them thought, "Some kind of dream, illusion, we get to Cuba and we get in a corner of a sugarcane field somewhere and we just start chopping. That's the type of life there'd be. That's all there was to it." He admitted it would have worked in Tahiti, or any other place as well. The idea of going to Cuba came to him while he was taking a course in Latin American history. He got the impression that Castro had improved the country, especially in comparison with other Latin American countries. He mentioned his fantasy to her, and she fanned it with helpless little questions like, "Could we really do that?" He would bravely reply, "Yes," and finally found himself committed to a course of action.

He was eager to leave the United States because he feared an armed conflict between the blacks and whites. "I think it will be a black-white revolution, but I don't know exactly how bloody it will be while it happens, or how effective it will be after it happens.

I'd be afraid of doing things, I don't particularly want to die. If the time came to shoot other people, I don't think I want to shoot anybody." Also, he wished to leave the country in order to avoid being drafted.

He was certain he could have killed for Gladys. "Her father's a very obnoxious person, and one day I just looked at him and knew I could kill him. Made me a little sick."

In the months prior to their departure, he became increasingly angry at the people who had let Gladys down. No one would ask her to play in the orchestra. Sometimes they were curt to her. Fantasies of mass destruction seized and disturbed him at such times.

About two months before their skyjacking attempt, they were insulted while walking down the street by two men in a pick-up truck yelling, "Which one is the guy?" and "She sure is ugly," and such. George, who usually ignored this type of incident, brought on by his long hair and his manner of dressing, yelled back at them. They jumped out of the truck and, to his surprise, George soundly beat them up. "I just felt completely like a machine, like I had no feelings whatsoever. This was just an operation that I was to perform. Afterward, I had the most incredible tightness and stiffness in my whole body. I felt myself completely rigid." He was badly frightened with the knowledge that he would *kill someone,* if they didn't leave the United States.

Not long after this, they began to discuss their going to Cuba seriously. "It was always a ridiculous possibility that was going to be tried. Perhaps the idea took a month and the preparation not more than two weeks. I had read a few things about Cuba. I knew that something had to happen. Otherwise, we were really going to start taking it out on each other. As for myself, it was time for me to do something. Well, here I'd been for twenty-one years just kind of *floating through the world,* walking around blah, blah, blah, not really getting anywhere, making any kind of decision or taking any kind of stand. It adds up to nothingness. A kind of follow-the-leader type of nothing. I think it's dangerous for people to break the chain out, but I think it's necessary. A chain is a kind of habitual low-energy living. Each day just breathing deeply enough to get enough oxygen to be able to move around, and you're always kind of blah. I'm that way, very stagnant type of person, kind of dragging around. I don't think it's any way to live, I think it's very, very tiring. In the same environment, anything will really irritate you. You begin to breathe deeply and to live on a higher energy level, and you can get excited about things. Things really tend to irritate you. A pack of cigarettes really makes you angry because you know that is part of what's hanging you in. All kinds of things that come along make you angry. You surround yourself with all these things that you're tying around your waist." He felt by breaking the chain he would be giving himself a chance "to be free of a lot of things that are encumbering."

"We thought it was a good idea in the first place, because of *the simplicity* of it and the almost nothingness that you had to do. You didn't have to really force anybody to do anything because the responsibility on them was so great, they weren't in a position to counteract it. I thought that was probably the best reason for doing this type of thing. Also because it was easy . . . I was kind of looking toward Cuba as the skyjacker, stealing, some kind of welcome. The downtrodden American fleeing the oppression of the capitalists and all that kind of thing. It became a romantic type of thing, the Holy Grail and that, the land of milk and honey, and all that type of stuff."

For weapons, they got a paring knife[2] from Gladys' mother's kitchen and bought a can of insecticide. She bought the ticket with funds in their joint account. They took a train to New York where they boarded the plane, sitting across the aisle from each other. When he decided it was time, "I really didn't feel much momentum getting up so I put my head down. I was going to count ten, and when I got to ten, stand up. I still didn't have much momentum. So I had to go all the way to about sixty and finally I opened my eyes and got up and walked through the curtains. I felt that this was something distasteful that had to be done. I remember feeling that I . . . that it would be humiliating not to. I think it was still the

---

2 The same knife used by Gladys' brother in his attempts to intimidate her.

right thing for me to do. At that time, I felt that I was finally taking control of my life."

"I guess I told them that this was a hijacking and I brandished my can at him [laughter]. And then told them, some kind of chemical was inside, better do as I wanted. They all spun around real quick and they were all unhappy. I thought they looked kind of groddy up close [laughter]. All these people spinning around in swivel chairs with ear phones turning around looking at me. It was really strange. I just felt confident that this was all there was to it. This was all I had to do." Then the crew began asking his name, his religion, his reasons for wanting to go to Cuba. "I thought, 'Now what is this? They're interrogating me.' And so I could feel *everything slipping away because I had nothing to hold on to* and that was it. I had already laid all my cards on the table and that was all I was going to do, walk in, brandish my knife, hold up the can, and that was the end of it. I'd done all I was ready to do. They had shut Gladys out of the cockpit and I was alone. So, after that, things were all down hill. They started to talk about headwinds, and lacking fuel, and all this kind of thing, and I was totally unprepared for that, but I said, 'Yeah, yeah, we'll see.' So we got near Miami and they said there wasn't enough fuel and we'd have to land in Miami and get fuel. They said they couldn't guarantee anything on the ground, and I said, 'Well, okay.' At first I'd been pretty mad at them because I'd wished he'd do it and get it over with."

George was definitely opposed to using the knife or any other form of physical violence. When the situation needed a show of strength, he was completely helpless, since they had shut Gladys out of the cockpit and he was alone. "A lot of people said, 'Why didn't you shoot him? Why didn't you stab him? Why didn't you let the stuff go?' That's how they think. I just couldn't do that. So there I was up against the wall and splattered. I just wanted Gladys and I just wanted to disappear and fade away into the walls or something."

He missed Gladys a great deal in prison and dreamed of her frequently. He felt that getting out of prison would be difficult for them, because the effort was all for nothing, and they would face the same problems again. "I feel in many ways I'm not capable of functioning." His feelings of physical heaviness were increasing in prison, as was his sense of separating from his body. "In many ways I allow myself to be a lot weaker. Because of lack of determination, lack of direction, a general fear of asserting myself. I think she acts as a catalyst for me, she gets me moving. Not necessarily in the direction of success, but she prods me onward."

When asked if he would care to send a message to Gladys, he called out her name, over and over and over and *over* and *over* again, "I love you, take care."

## General Comments

Gladys' description of her experience on the roller coaster made one of the most important contributions to my forthcoming work on the emotion of motion. It was the play of children, employing a vertical axis as on swings, teeter-totters, slides, etc., that first led my thought into this area. Interestingly enough, it led Michael Balint into similar country, so that he came to wonder if there was not a way in which one might divide most people into two groups.[3] Members of one group have a tendency to cling; Balint called them ocnophiles. Those in the second group have a tendency to jump, and he called them philobats. He felt that the latter, like acrobats, trusted space and urged themselves as far as possible into it. The former, on the other hand, saw space as a "horrid thing" to be avoided at all costs. Balint was also of the opinion that just as people move their physical bodies about in these ways, so too do they treat their thoughts. But he said that he could not find the appropriate language in which to express himself on the matter.

Much has been written about the multiple ways in which a mutual interlocking of personality factors takes place between couples. It is often pointed out how the needs of one partner are fulfilled by the abilities of the other. Various people who are familiar with the case of Gladys and George tend to identify with one or the other on

[3] Michael Balint, "Friendly Expanses—Horrid Empty Spaces," *The International Journal of Psycho-Analysis*, 36 (1955), 225–241.

the grounds that one partner was "really living off" the other and vice versa.

I do not see the matter that way at all. To me, the two are balanced in their relationship, in that each gave to the other and took from the other. Without doubt, the relationship was the best and the healthiest that either one has ever had. Growth, in varying degrees, has been evident, the skyjacking to the contrary notwithstanding.

It is noteworthy that the knife George used to threaten the stewardess was the one used by Gladys' brother years before. This time it was held by the man Gladys had chosen as her lover, and she gave it to him at the moment when she was searching her mind for "the most dangerous and threatening thing she could think of."

## About Rape

A sexual factor is obvious in skyjacking. Essentially, only men do it. Up to this point in the study, I had been convinced of a sexual factor, and saw it to be an unconscious "rape," performed by a very timid man.

Suddenly, this double case posed a problem, prior to the interview. What was a woman doing at the site of another woman's rape? The answer is quite simple. The actual crime of physical rape occasionally occurs under circumstances in which the rapist is accompanied by a female friend, who often even helps to hold the victim. Two things are usually true of such female helpers: first they have, themselves, been the victim of rape and sexual abuse as children, and second, they are concerned about their "man's" lack of manhood. In the first instance, they wish to retroject their experience into another woman, in order to be done with it. (The choice of the knife, here, involves an almost poetic coincidence.) In the second instance, they want the experience to be "added to" the man's image of himself, as an introject. These considerations had been explained to my secretaries, prior to the interviews, so that when they typed the tapes they accused me of writing a script for the prisoners.

Of some interest are a few of the projective test responses given by Gladys. From the point of view of my study, all of her responses are interesting, but only these few are included. Charles H. Holland, Ph.D., Assistant Professor of Psychology at Hollins College, kindly provided the testing.

### THEMATIC APPERCEPTION TEST

*Card 3BM*—"They're moving in on him . . . his head is spinning . . . he's got his track shoes on, his sneaks, and he's running fast."

*Card 13MF*—He's "wondering why he always has these dizzy spells when something important is happening. . . ."

### RORSCHACH TEST

*Card X*—Second response—rotated 180°. "A crevice, something like Grand Canyon . . . insects are throwing things into it and two men are following . . . both holding hands . . . MAN! . . . mean looking, that guy [the King]. [Canyon with feeling of depth . . . men holding a statue] . . . makes me want to jump in, like at the Lincoln Center balcony."

## About George and Politics

George was the only man in the series who even vaguely might have been considered to be a *political rebel*. But it was largely front, to conceal his fears. What his case does do, though, is to clearly drive home the fact that, even if one of these men had been a screaming Communist menace, loudly proclaiming the virtues of Marx at the time of his crime, it would have meant exactly nothing. *These men, in spite of their conscious rationalizations, are moved by forces much more primitive and powerful than political thought.* This must be borne in mind, when the opportunity arises to study cases presenting a surface political rationalization. Simply put, any man, be he Democrat, Republican, royalist, Communist, Fascist, or nihilist, will, in the long run, commit his crime for the reasons set forth here, rather than for the *obvious* facts he, and we, have believed motivated him.

An effort to obtain cooperation of foreign psychiatrists, to examine *their* offenders in *their* own native languages, is to be made. The contents of this study will have been presented to the Third International Congress of Social Psychiatry in Dubrovnik, Yugoslavia, before this book is published. It is strongly hoped that, if such men are carefully and knowingly studied, it will be found that they are close kinsmen to our own offenders. This would completely smash the myth of the political nature of the crime, destroy the premise for "political asylum," and open the way toward medical diplomacy. This would end the entire matter. *Not one man in the series felt he would have committed the crime, if he had known he would be returned on the same plane.* The hostile barrier between nations is the critical social factor, just as it was in their original families.

# XI

# A Trio of Patients

## THE CASE OF DAN

Dan was twenty-two years old, black, and single. He came from a Southern family characterized by strife and instability. He was the only child.

He was apparently bright and aggressive in the pre-school period. He and his parents lived quite near a parochial school, which he attended from the first grade. About the time Dan entered school, his father left his mother after a sustained fight. At that time the boy believed that it was expected of him to make a choice between his parents. Although he could not get along with his father, he did not understand the necessity for choosing between them. He elected to stay with his mother. "Father was drinking all the time, and there was no man or no manly figure, so I tried to prove I was a man." He took up sports to prove this. He said his mother did not understand him.

"I had a cousin who was like a brother. We are still close. He is older than I, and I look up to him."

"For eight years my life was tied up with nuns at the parochial school. It was very good there. There were presents at Christmas. But I was very nervous. I would eat, get sick, and vomit. I was also nervous around a lot of people." He was bright and a good student, except in math.

In grade school, he sustained a head injury in football and "felt like someone else. I often felt others wouldn't do what I would do.

151

My mother said I was 'so different.' After the 'new guy' I fell off in school work." He was previously compulsively studious, but now school mattered less. He started wanting to drop out in junior high school. Up until then, his school record was "beautiful, very high."

"I haven't been happy in the last few years. After I was hurt, I sort of felt depressed. I saw people with nicer clothes and cars. I used to value my *intelligence,* but my values changed.

"I wanted to work in missiles and be a space man. This was a childish dream. I could see myself in the Air Force. I followed all the space shots closely. Once without being asked to do so, I lectured for a whole day [a month before his skyjacking] on the space program. Everybody was *amazed* at the knowledge I had amassed. I showed slides and lectured each class on the hour. They were *amazed* and called me the 'space man.' I'm not as interested now as when I was a kid, because then I could see myself as a success. Now I want to go into medicine rather than aeronautics."

He joined the Army to get away from home. He did not like school, or the teachers, and was not a success with girls. He was seeking manhood in the Army. He did not like what he saw in the Army and tried to overlook his dislikes until he could take it no longer. "Shouts and guns, soldiers are supposed to like guns and take orders."

He could not rebel. Stationed in Europe, he was fighting and drinking heavily. He would report to sick call and then to drinking. He did not go looking for girls. He was court-martialed for "unprovoked attacks." "I just felt I had to do them. I hated the Army." It did not take much to provoke Dan to attack. "Once in a bar, a girl tapped me on the shoulder. She thought she knew me or liked me. I tried to cut her with a knife, but a fellow kept me from it. I told a psychiatrist I was going to do something desperate. I hated the Army and was getting angrier."

When he was in school, he used to be ashamed of his clothes. Now, he used his Army pay to "buy clothes, be a big shot, $100 suits." Discharge from the service threw him back into his old poverty.

He was in a VA hospital just before skyjacking, on a diagnosis of a "nervous breakdown." "I hid lots of thoughts out of shame from the doctors. I was hearing voices, and saw optical illusions at night." He had the same symptoms before his discharge from the Army, but refused to go to the hospital for a year after his release.

Dan was home on a ninety-day leave from the hospital when "my mother also had a nervous breakdown. She broke the windows in her church. The pastor arrested her, and they put her in jail. I wanted to kill someone. Wished I had had a gun, I'd have killed them. She was so good. I was especially proud of her. I never argued with her until I was hurt. I curse her now and can't help myself. I'm ashamed of it. After I was released from the Army, I was scared I'd hurt her or kill her if I got angry and hit her. I can't stop after I start.

"You could say I had thought of hijacking for months. I started planning, but I had no money and no job. When she was to be released from the hospital, I had to get away. Once before I ran away to Atlanta for three months with my cousin. Mother wrote and asked me to come back, and I went home because *she* said so. It was the same thing, *prison,* my *prison.* I felt people were watching me all the time. There was something *different* about me, the way I walked or talked. There were eyes on me all the time.

"The night after she came home from the hospital, I sneaked out of the house at 3:00 A.M. and took a bus to Atlanta. I had to get out. She had come back from the hospital. I remembered her other breakdown when I was ten, and I just couldn't take it again. High! Fearful, she'd cry and cry. I never forgot that. Years later, she had another breakdown. The day she came home I hijacked. I broke into the dresser and stole cash. I went to Atlanta and intuitively ran into my kinfolk. Then I was scared they'd [mother] come get me and *nag* some more. I couldn't take that. I felt they'd have to kill me to take me back. That's what drove me, because I couldn't go back to that place.

"I got a .22 pistol from where my cousin kept it. I told them I was going to California and they drove me to the airport. I told them I had a job. They thought I was a writer.

"I was sitting in my seat, gun in my pocket, very shaky. I felt

I shouldn't do it. I couldn't make myself get up, and I was shaking like I was cold. I pulled the gun on the stewardess and she jumped. It made me feel better that I could scare her. The pilot didn't say to put it down. I bluffed him. Nobody gave me any static. In a way, it disappointed me that no one said for me to put the gun down or to go to my seat. They took it like a carnival ride, like 'everyday.' I don't know."

It gave him a feeling of power, power of life and death, like a "big shot."

He was hospitalized in Cuba. "The Cubans were angry at me. There was no political gain in me. They just tried to help keep me from the United States. They didn't have good relations with the United States." He was given shock treatment and group therapy. "They shaved my head, used electrodes." He had five EST treatments in three months. Eventually, he was sent to Europe, turned himself in in West Berlin, and was returned to the United States.

"I don't know about the future. I don't worry or think about it. I want to leave again, but not by hijacking. Abroad I found a girl I want to marry."

## General Comments

This case came to my attention shortly after the hush-hush restriction on my studies of skyjackers. Consequently, interviewing Dan was a first effort by a colleague who was just beginning to grasp the essentials of the method and of the search for specifics.

I might note that we did observe the amenities of the "ban" on my activities. I was not told that the man was in the hospital. I did not interview him. They did not send me the taped interview until after Dan had left the hospital. We could have done a better job on this case without the restriction.

## THE CASE OF FRANK

Frank manifested social and physical disorientation. He was filled with rage over his ineptitude and failure, and driven toward an unmanageable anger whose consequences would probably result in "sin," in terms of the ethic under which he was raised. He solved his problem by "flight" and the creation of interpersonal distance.

Frank had not been tried yet, and his attorney had called to ask me to see him in prison. The attorney said Frank was "just a good-old-southern-nigger."

In the jail, as the guard was leading us to a conference room with Frank walking in front of me, I observed that he walked in the loose-jointed, "high-stepping" way of the rural Negro, but that it seemed to shield a network of tight restraint underneath. I had the feeling that he did not like to have people behind him.

When we entered the interview room, I offered him a chair and started to unload my gear. He did not sit down, but stood with his back to the wall, placing himself closer to the door than I was. His refusal to sit down was barely concealed by the pretense that he had failed to understand the invitation.

His hands were unusual, in the same way as the hands of many process schizophrenics are unusual. His fingers were fully extended —or mildly hyperextended—jutting from a rigid hand anchored in an unbending wrist. The effect was that of a fan or a club. Such hands seem to indicate that they were never involved enough with the outside world to fall into the fixed "work curve" of most hands. Such hands seem never to have done anything effectively. Frank's approach to the paper work displayed the ineptness of such hands. He did a great deal of "country fanning" of the papers as he importantly brushed away non-existent obstacles to his work. The tight skin over his fingers never crinkled, because he did not flex the joints.

He clung dependently to the left edge of the papers. In many instances, he timidly placed his hand in the space between his paper and the test card, in order to trace the outline with his finger. But his hand was turned palm up, so that he haltingly traced the outline with the back of his finger! This hand position seemed to have been designed to conceal or deny the intended action.

The Bender-Gestalt was clearly more than Frank could cope with. He felt compelled to try to count things, but would "lose his place" even with the outstretched fingers. Angular structures tended to turn into curves. Controlled curves on the other hand tended to become misplaced so that he was often obliged to create sharp angles to "get back in line." He made many erasures as he realized gross errors in the number of curves. He did not perceive differences in linear length or sharpness of angulation. Completing the test required three to four times longer than normal. By the time he finished, he was tired and his palms were so wet he had to rub them on his shirt to dry them.

The next test was no less troublesome. The test was a 16 P. F., which reveals something about anxiety in people who mismanage space when anxious. It usually requires thirty to forty-five minutes. Again, Frank had trouble "keeping his place," as he tried to move his eyes from the question sheet to the answer sheet. Again, he used the unbending hand as a denied pointer, with which he created the image of disjointed movement. At the same time this hand was used to conceal his test responses from my eyes. He agonized over questions that required "Yes," "I don't know," or "No" answers. He needed over an hour and forty-five minutes to complete the test.

From the moment of our first contact, he had been eyeing my tape recorder as if it were some sort of highly dangerous object. As I set the volume controls, he refused another cigarette, even though he had been smoking steadily. He was obviously prepared for trouble and seemed almost to flinch when I moved even slightly.

The oral interview was brief and dramatic. He said he was twenty-nine years old, born in the South, the fifth and youngest child of his parents. All four siblings were sisters, and he was disinclined to speak about them. His father was "okay," he stated evasively. (He hung his head as if he felt guilty even about speaking of him.) His mother was also "okay," and she was in charge of the family discipline. Inquiry here led to a blurted reply that "at least *she* wasn't violent." When asked why he chose the word "violent," he pulled away from the microphone. He put his head down and began to mutter as if he were speaking to someone under the table. Then, he said in an ordinary voice, "I told them," as if he were responding to a questioner beside him rather than to me across the desk. Suddenly, he blocked. I probably forced it by saying he should speak up, because his attorneys had asked me to see if I could help him. He roared, then slammed his hands on the table to announce that he "didn't like whites," and that he was "tired of being pushed around and cursed by them."

He was terrified at being so angry in a tight place. Apparently, he knew from experience that he could not control this type of anger. He solved the problem by the rapid creation of space between us, as he sprang to the door and *ran* back to the safety of his cell.

There is so much about this interview to remind one of the works of Miller and Zarcone, and of Balint, in spite of its lack of personal information.

## THE CASE OF RAFE

Rafe was thirty-five years of age. He spoke rapidly and with much assurance in a loud, clear voice. From the beginning of the interview, he attempted to assume a superior, didactic role, in contrast to other offenders.

He was the second of four sons. One was three years older than himself, one eighteen months younger, and one six years younger.

His father was a very successful professional man who had worked his way through professional school, married well, and was moving "upward" at a rapid rate. The son describes him as "being very straight, very puritanical, and worked his ass off. The discipline, strangely enough, he enforced verbally but never physically. He lived it to a certain degree."

The mother "had been raised in the Church of Christ and then the Methodist. She had been pampered as a child. She did all the discipline. Dad was generous to a fault. He had such low self-worth. He felt he had to buy everything he got."

The patient's earliest memories were of "being lifted by an aunt to look into what appeared to be a very high bird bath at one year and nine months. Another was of sitting on what looked like an immensely high ceiling with a skylight. I was sure it was big enough to swallow me up. I was walking at the time. I was quite proud of my walking. I managed to put my feet forward straight and it was commented that my older brother did it slew-footed. I had a foot problem, flat feet. I had to wear special shoes. I was quite proud of them." His earliest recollected dream was a nightmare. "Actually, I believed at the time that there was a witch unmanifest which was chasing me. I was sitting in a chair. You know those puffballs you step on in the woods and whoosh? It is the witch manifest. The casters, the rollers on the chair, would almost touch these little puffballs and I knew if they touched, the witch would puff out and get me. I didn't try to move. I didn't try to move. I'm sure that must have been it. I knew I was terrified, but I couldn't seem to do anything."

The children were raised mostly by the servants. The mother was described as being attractive, vivacious, and fun to be with, except when problems arose which she simply couldn't cope with.

Rafe felt that he was being victimized by his older brother by means of his superior intelligence. "He would make me feel stupid or unwanted and I already had enough of that from the first man in my life. I was very sensitive to that kind of conversation. My mother told me, 'Well, there's only one way to combat that, ignore it.' We had a big house and he was trying to get me to do something. He could usually force me to do things verbally with the threat of force behind it, of course, so I just ignored it. I didn't answer him. It infuriated him so badly that he almost had a fit right on the spot. I remember it as a moment of strange victory because I didn't understand it at all."

In contrast, his relationship with the younger brother who was closest to himself in size, was a "very close one for a long time. We were like the Corsican brothers. I think, but I don't really know this for a fact, Doctor, I've always had a suspicion that a lot of damage [to me] had been done already by the time he was born. I loved him and yet I wanted to hurt him and I often did, and God, the pangs of guilt I would go through. I would take something that was his and withhold it from him by virtue of superior size and watch him suffer. We played great jokes on each other. When he defecated in the woods, I gave him poison ivy to wipe his ass with." There was no particular relationship between Rafe and his youngest brother.

He felt that the mother displayed no favoritism, but he believed he was the father's favorite. He recalled without affect that his mother always saw him as a problem child. The other brothers all became successful lawyers although Rafe feels all have exhibited relative instability, but "They were not as intense as perhaps I am."

He recalled another recurring dream which, as nearly as it could be traced, occurred after the dreams of paralysis but before he started school. "I had the power to fly. I could fly wherever I wanted to. In one dream, I was at my grandfather's farm working in the field with an old colored man. I just received my first pair of work boots and I was very proud of them. I recall I wanted to see the whole farm, but I wanted to see it like a bird so I went out and started flapping my arms [flaps arms]. I was flapping my arms and when I started to rise, I realized I didn't have to flap my arms so I stopped flapping my arms. I rose without control. I could go this way or that way by twisting my body. In this way, I found that my thoughts controlled my direction in dreams, and once I discovered that, I carried it with me into my waking hours and remembered that all I had to do was to think a place and I could go there. This dream continued until last year, but the pattern has changed from flights of fancy to flights of learning. Last night I visited, by what could be called astro-travel if you were familiar with it, a certain place in India near New Delhi. I'm so new at this, but I work up feelings and find a blissful feeling of quiet and peace. This was last night."

The patient felt that sensations of paralysis and of falling preceded the genesis of his flying dreams, particularly a dream at age four when he was drowning in the ocean. He felt helpless, ineffective, and unable to buoy himself up.

Rafe felt that the falling dream has often been forced upon him. For example, "I would fall, and realize that I was falling, and realize that I had to fly to preserve myself. So I would fly." He often dreamed of "being unable to move to save someone, or speak out quickly enough. The feeling was of being ineffective."

He claimed that he clearly remembered going to the beds of various mature women in his home at ages four and five. They pretended to be asleep while he fondled their breasts or vaginas. He did not recall ever having feared the Devil. He was raised as a Protestant, but was offended by the social aspects of religion. "I have always believed that there was something deeper than this outward form of worship, that man is very close to being his own God if he wants to be." This mystic strain later carried him toward Hinduism.

He believed that at age six he would have been described as a problem child. He painted the neighbors' cars, turned in false alarms, and peeked through keyholes at people in tubs and beds throughout the house.

Then, his sexual curiosity "went underground" until about age ten, when it was reactivated by masturbation. During the interim period, he started public school, was shifted to a private school, and then to a military school. He "had a short memory span, was attention-craving by outlandish acts and speech, a screaming case of low–self-worth."

In military school, he had his first experiences with homosexuality and was discharged on account of them at age eleven. In the brace of schools he attended (fourteen for twelve grades), he performed acts of bravery. "Without any visible forms of support, I'd swim two to five miles without even knowing whether I could." He smoked in order to rebel and was generally defiant of authority. By the tenth grade, he felt he had established a deep "failure pattern," as a means of "getting their attention" by forcing them to "bail him out." After the homosexual period from nine to eleven, his sexuality went underground again beneath the rebellious cover. Of his interest in girls, he said of himself at thirteen, "I was very slow in those days."

As a junior in high school, he and a friend, on a trip, got a "hooker" in a hotel. "I didn't know what to do and she must have sensed it because she helped me out." Socially, he was slow with girls his own age, although by fifteen he had resumed his nocturnal visits to the rooms of older women in the home. His dreams, both awake and asleep, of free flight to distant parts of the world continued uninterrupted during this time. He felt his control of direction by mental self-discipline was increasing his directional skills.

In his fifteenth year, a new recurring dream appeared; this too has persisted, although it gradually varied. In this dream, he reported, "I am hooded like a monk, but my hood is down. There is another figure similar in garb but with his hood up. We are standing on a slight rise and walk down a path onto a plain. The path forks and a cow path goes toward a lamasery and a broad road toward a brightly lighted distant city. Walking and talking with the other figure, I experience an immense peace. At the fork in the path the other figure says to me (without turning), 'Which way will you go?' and then he turns and it is me."

In the variation of this dream, the topics of discussion with the other figure have become less general. Specific discussions have led him to stop smoking abruptly, to begin vegetarian diets, etc.

This sense of duality has been present frequently. While awake during dissociative moments, "One part of me would watch while I did some damn fool thing and make no effort to save me."

After graduation from high school, there were several ill-fated attempts at various colleges, each of which ended in disaster because of Rafe's inability to organize and his continuing pattern of theatrical acting-out. He enlisted in the Air Corps. There he associated "with members of a homosexual clique, because I could always hold off. It didn't attract me in terms of physical contact, but for the attention I got for it. I never did come through. I was seeking attention from men like what I didn't get from my father." In time, the Air Force discharged him on the grounds of homosexuality.

Following the discharge, he resumed the abortive collegiate pattern, showing interest chiefly in theatrical activities. Here he met the girl who was to become his wife. "It started with, 'I've got to impress her,' and then that old passivity sense, and the masculine side of her, and we were off. She had been abused by her father, so she just dominated [me] and that was all." The marriage was rough, with his being "led around by the nose for years." Then followed a period when they took turns at leading. After much effort, labor, and therapy, they arrived at a situation where he leads and she says, "My man, right or wrong."

The marriage was quite difficult in other ways, with multiple infidelities on his part. Each was a deep emotional involvement in which he ran from his wife to another woman. Each was always preceded by his projected feelings associated with his mother toward his wife—feelings that activated considerable hostility in him. The hostility, in turn, served as his justification for abusing her and the children.

His father died when Rafe was twenty-two. He was already married at that time and had a two-year-old daughter. "Do you love me?" he asked his father as he lay dying. His grief was short-lived.

Rafe went into various businesses, each of which held his interest only for a very brief period. He sought psychiatric help on an individual basis a number of times and on other occasions through group therapy together with his wife. For a two-year period he held down a job as a reporter, but he was often deeply disappointed by his self-diagnosed failure as a workman. He often copied the work of other reporters. At such moments, he was seized by the familiar dissociative phenomenon wherein one part of him stood apart viewing with disgust but no desire to restrain the other part.

Then, he worked for five years as a free-lance public relations man, but derived little gratification from his labors. He charged less than his services were worth, because he could not tolerate the tension of competitive pricing. During this period, he continued with various psychotherapies, extended his studies of Hinduism, and worked at meditation.

He described meditation as "a deliberate total detachment from the body. Beginning first with prayer in the lotus position, the body is allowed to slump into a fixed posture. Breathing is then controlled, and various parts of the body are shut off by deliberate concentration. The eyes are closed to shut out vision and the ears ignore sound, whereas the tongue is pressed to the palate to eliminate taste." When all else is suspended, "The difficult trick is the worst of all—to quiet your mind." As the "prayer becomes more manifest, the meditation deepens and the whole system seems to withdraw you—it is a definite physical sensation."

The sensation is, "Do you remember the first time you ever kissed a girl and your stomach went up to your . . . ? Okay, this is a small part of it, but this seems to radiate in all directions, Doctor. This is part of it. Another part is that your body, although outwardly dormant, seems inwardly quite alive, not in the need to move muscularly but in its ability to sense its own faults, as if there were some like sores. In a sense you almost get the impression that you can rush aid to an afflicted area. I don't know if it is true or not, but you get the feeling that you could. There is another very distinct sensation in the medulla, right back here, and it comes from the spine. The radiation begins in the solar plexus. It moves downward and it moves upward. It moves from the diaphragm. It goes and it can be felt, Doctor, like goosebumps. No goosebumps arise, by the way, but it is the same type of sensation. It is quite distinctive, no mistaking it. You can feel this sensation of heat in the medulla and, Doctor, I cannot describe what happens after that. It is indescribable. It is uplifting. It is euphoric, no question, and yet practical, not some fanatical thing. There are no fantasies. There are no mental images, no pictures associated with this feeling."

It was his ambition to create a retreat or sanctuary to which tired and defeated men could go to relax and rediscover themselves. Diet and meditation, along with love and tender care, were regarded by Rafe as aids to releasing creative impulses in such men.

Whenever he was particularly upset, he used to take long drives. "Driving is a series of automated responses that require, believe it or not, much less attention than you are taught to believe. So, when all of your motor functions are there occupied, you'll find you're strangely free, to concentrate on something utterly unrelated to driving." He also liked to walk a great deal for the same reasons. He spoke of a "discharge from walking."

He derived a certain sense of satisfaction from the manipulation of power in behalf of his clients, but not enough money or recognition. The assassinations of Kennedy and King proved to him that the nation was losing its moral fiber. An outbreak of black power militancy in his city frightened him, and he moved his family to a campsite out of town to protect them from violence. "There was the feeling that something was terribly wrong."

Feeling that when things are wrong, the first rule of life is to "change oneself," he and his wife—feeling that they had finished with psychotherapy by then—"began to look objectively for a solution. We were not satisfied with the shabby, shoddy values that we found in American life."

They decided to leave city life and camp out in the country where they could concentrate on proper food, fresh air, and hard work, because "lots of these things are character-building." He was excited by the possibilities of the move, but was also in terror of the responsibilities. "I wasn't sure I had the balls to hack it." They set up tents in a wooded area and enrolled the children in public school in the fall of 1968. He intended to work as a freelance photographer.

His response to this radical change in their living arrangements was twofold. He felt he had "made the break" and was "excited by the potential." On the other hand, he was "queasy and a little afraid." After a short time, he found he was "projecting mother at my wife again like a fucking yo-yo, and drawing closer and closer" to his daughter, who was fifteen years old at the time. He could not understand what was happening to him, "what was wrong." He discontinued taking the tranquilizer prescribed for him, although he ought to have learned from repeated experience the consequences of discontinuing it. Invariably, he tended toward "non-stop thinking, which is like trying to stop a turbine," to bring it to a halt.

In this instance, the non-stop thought was of "balling" his daughter. He was in a state of stimulation from wanting to "ball her," and at the same time he was filled with doubt that he "had the balls to hack" his job. They were completely out of money.

They all lived in one tent, and it was difficult, if not impossible, to have intercourse with his wife. Rafe felt that he "had no immediate discharge in spite of having this big load on." His sensuality was, he felt, "directed downward instead of upward." He felt his "brain was getting overfed, overcharged, and cross-circuited somehow."

His first idea for easing this dilemma was to move away from the family until he cooled off, but he knew that he would "want to come right back again." Then, it occurred to him that if he went to Cuba, he would not be permitted to return. He was frightened by the possibility of the death penalty. He bought a tear-gas–filled fountain pen, and forced a pilot to take him to Cuba.

On the descent for landing in Cuba he "discharged, total discharge. Like all of a sudden the mastoid area loosened behind the ears, the frontal lobes cleared so abruptly, so suddenly that my sinuses contracted. There was a breaking and a rush, just like that" [snaps fingers]. This reaction terminated the moment he saw men with guns and "didn't know what to expect."

His first response was to tighten up, and then very quickly he needed to talk. As soon as it became apparent that his hosts were giving him the VIP treatment, he experienced a sudden massive lethargy, "like I hadn't slept in years and was going to sleep for years. Terrific hunger—they fed me. I had often gone hungry on purpose and learned to ward off the awareness of hunger. Fish, fresh fish at that, fried. Beautiful. Lots of vegetables and Cuban coffee. I laid down on the floor and went to sleep."

After his reception in Cuba, he made a serious effort to adapt himself to his new situation by "divorcing myself for the moment from guilt and all the rest of it. I wanted to learn and traveled a lot."

By virtue of a chance encounter, he realized that he had "made a monumentally wrong decision." One evening, accompanied by his guard, he went to an amusement park, saw some girls, and picked one up "to ball her and for some fun." When he asked the girl her age and she replied she was fourteen, he felt "as if a thunderclap had hit me. Fourteen, my God, what am I doing here?" He immediately found an excuse to "go back to my house which was miles away. I walked and walked and walked, kept this poor bastard [guard] up most of the night. He kept saying, *Que pasa?"* It suddenly occurred to him that "this was why I had left America. Hung up on my daughter, which can only mean one thing: I still haven't totally defeated my homosexuality. I haven't got rid of the internal momma I keep loading on my wife." He decided he had to come home and face it in spite of the death penalty.

To that end, he provoked the Cubans by calling them "infantile idiots with pistols," whereupon they refused to let him take his regular walks, which were quite important to him. He then demanded to be returned to the States. There were delays, and there was more anger, after which he spent a month in jail. Eventually, he was placed aboard a ship for Canada. After he arrived there, he found himself so affected by the sensation of shipboard motion that he had the optical illusion of movement for over a week. For more than a month, he walked with a "wide-legged movement as though I was still on shipboard, because my head was still moving inside as if it were." After a time, things "settled down" and he crossed the barrier.

After trial, conviction, and transfer to prison, Rafe summed up his attitude: "When I came back, it was because I was determined to be a victor yet. Doctor, I am a victor and proud of it. I have sweated blood over this victory." He takes cold showers, vigorously exercises, and employs diet and meditation in his attempt to do without the leveling effect of the tranquilizer. He does not want a perpetual crutch.

## General Comments

Rafe represents the best probability in our sample of a potential disturbance of vestibular function. Unfortunately, methods presently available for studying vestibular function are inadequate.

Even lay readers will almost certainly conclude that Rafe is by no means a "normal" person. Is it only chance that attorneys refer to psychotics as "unbalanced"? Yet the possibility of studying him properly with the ultimate purpose of helping him and others with comparable problems is nil, the way things are. He was found to be sane at the time of his crime, and at the time of his trial, and he will be unavailable for the duration of his twenty-year sentence. I find it incomprehensible that our Medical Center has not been able to perform even such basic, elementary tests as the Caloric Stimulation or the Baranay for lack of adequate personnel and equipment. The solution to the overriding social problem of finding means to reconcile the requirements of penal restriction and medical research in a sanely pragmatic fashion can be only a subject of fantasy at the present time.

Months ago, we concluded an agreement with the Department of Neurology at Northwestern University Medical School, to do all of those highly complex studies of these men, which are indicated. At this time, there is not the slightest possibility that the government will permit us to move these men for even five days to do such tests. Not even in the national interest. The arrangement as made would have cost the government nothing (the cost would have been met by private donors) and would not have violated the security requirements.

In point of fact, we can't even borrow bank robbers with comparable evidence of equilibratory studies. It is not that the men are unwilling, because all are volunteers. It is simply fear of the unknown on the part of the administrators.

## Levitation

En route to the city where this man was to be interviewed, I idly flipped through a current issue of *Life* magazine. Suddenly, a full two-page spread of a fuzzily ethereal sketch of a winged man (Icarus, Daedalus, or Prometheus?) caught my eye. In a lower corner, in brave and alluring type, it said:

Come.
We will be your wings.
We will set you free.
Free beyond the heights of man.
Free to chase the sun.    Hug a cloud.

And, though you were born on earth.   To live on earth.
You will be at home, here in the sky.
The comfort and ease you own on earth, you will have up here.
And, Eastern will make it so.
It shall be a most natural thing.   For you.   To fly.
EASTERN   The Wings of man.

I leaned back and let them do all of these things for me.

After landing, I interviewed the patient just described, who can fly even when awake, and then went to my hotel. By chance, I stayed at the Regency-Hyatt, a really stunning place whose airy treatment of space is like no other I have ever seen. The hotel is built in a square, twenty stories high, and all of the rooms are on the outside. The hallways thus become verandas, each of which has its rooms on the outside, and they hold in their grip a gigantic roofed open space in the middle. The elevators are all glass and move up one wall of the space to permit a clear view and a sense of flight during ascent and descent.

The bellboy answered my query by saying that several people had jumped to their deaths from the *outside* of the structure, but that none had done so from the *inside*. Curious.

After dinner that evening, I floated (arose, flew, levitated, transcended, etc.) to my room via the astroview elevator-levitator. I skimmed (floated, wafted) my way along the terrace to my room (father has many of these in his mansion). It was still early, so I flipped on the television to see the news. The Apollo XII mission was underway and it provided endless views of "floating, weightless, gravity-free flight" and of the general good humor of the astronauts, and stimulated all kinds of feelings and images of what was yet to come. I steadied my dancing carcass as best I could.

Fortunately, a television commercial came on. It was about a children's food supplement and began with a distant shot of the little dears running and jumping as they approached the camera. At a certain point, by a clever technique of substitution of images, the children *became astronauts* who then bounded free of gravity all over the place. (So every red-blooded young soul who wishes to do so may be transformed in the twinkling of an eye into a Superman, a Buck Rogers, or a Flash Gordon.)

Feeling a little "light" at the moment, I placed my tape recorder in my lap as ballast.

The commercial changed. This one was on behalf of my "friendly carrier," Eastern Airlines. Somehow, they had got that ethereal man (Icarus, Daedalus, Prometheus?) out of *Life* magazine and covered him with dirty underwear and lots of feathers for wings. He was standing on a rocky crag from which he peered down on the mortals below. Then, he flung himself cleanly out into space, gliding first this way and then that. Then with the inevitable flair of cameramen who mean to show the dead "rising to their Maker," the camera panned upward into the cloud into which our winged one disappeared. Throughout the performance a honey-voiced announcer trickled treacle which said:

Come.
We will be your wings. . . .

Well! I put my suitcase on top of the tape recorder to add ballast and to create a writing surface. My notes of that moment run as follows:

Is it possible that Eastern Airlines compounds its problems by its saturation technique through which exactly the contents of the typical delusions of most skyjackers are thrust upon an unwary public? Is it chance that they have the highest rate of involvement and have been the first to employ the snooper-trooper and profile?

During our interview of Rafe, he was asked if he had ever seen this particular television commercial. He retorted contemptuously, "Yeah, *wings*."

On the flight back to Dallas, I moved rather slowly. My pockets were full of lead sinkers, as a protective measure. Quite aside from the humor involved here, this material can be most disturbing. After a lecture at Kansas University Medical School on the subject, in which many of the words to be described later as "crypto-vestibular speech" were used, several psychiatric residents were overheard complaining of vertigo. Several readers who have read a full collection of the material suffered the same symptom. When Dr. Don Johnston first really understood the material, he "flew for several weeks." Frankly, there have been moments when it upset me too, especially at first.

# XII
## Four Brief Case Reviews

Sixteen cases have been described in some detail at this point. If the reader does not suspect there *could be something important in further study* of these men, a few more cases won't help.

However, there are four cases left. They will be described in as little space as is possible in order to include their particular variations.

### THE CASE OF JUAN

The patient's mother died when he was four and his father died when the patient was five. He became so emotionally blunted by these events that he almost never dreamed, and he had few childhood memories. He was very hard to interview.

After the father's death, the patient lived with an aunt and uncle until the uncle was sent to prison for *raping* the patient's sister. The uncle died in prison. The patient moved, to live with a childless aunt.

In the Army, he had been a parachutist. He fled this country to Cuba, at a time when he felt obliged to *kill* either his wife, who had *cuckolded* him, or the Judge, who had "screwed him" with an alimony judgment for fifty dollars a month more than he made.

171

## THE CASE OF ERIC

For the most part, this man offered the usual picture of violent father, zealot mother. He had a little brother, to whom he was exceedingly protective.

He was in his seventies. It may be that a man of that age is totally different from other men, maybe not. His dreams were about the same, but his earliest recollections had a pungently different tone. They were all of motion, but it was all angular. He recalled his "favorite activity to be whirling on a truck wheel. I remember, there was one truck that was turned upside down and I used to get a big thrill by going to that lot and getting on the large hind wheel, and wrapping my body sort of around the hub, and spinning on it. I don't know if anyone ever saw me, but I often used to do that."

He also recalled "being sent for three cents worth of milk, with a can with a handle on it. I'd stay in the middle and swing it around and around." The last of his three first recollections, which tumbled all in a row upon inquiry, was of a steam engine. "I would sit on the floor for hours and watch that thing work [Go around]." While speaking of these memories, he became quite excited and used exaggerated circular hand movements to demonstrate the motion.

When the patient married, his wife assumed a controlling hostile attitude toward him. It was identical with the previous role of his father. As the patient said of them both, "They'd tell me I was full of shit [impractical]." They held him down, though, enough to go through life as a semi-failure instead of a complete one. When his wife died, he became like a machine without a governor and flew off, first into a wildly delusional state, and finally, in a plane toward Cuba.

## THE CASE OF SVEN

Sven was a middle-aged European, whose parents had the usual hostile cleft between them. It was based on sharp religious, social, and *political* differences, like those that occur when several small, proud nations are combined to forge a new European state.

The note of particular interest was his involvement with hostile borders. While in Europe, on two separate occasions, he flew wildly and illegally across national borders. He served a two-year sentence for the first offense, and three years for the second. His flights always followed acute failures as a husband.

This tendency to plunge back and forth across national boundaries is reminiscent of information gained from the State Department, about the Cubans, who skyjacked our planes to Cuba. Most of them were not men who had come to this country by the more common and legal routes. Instead, they had originally fled Cuba by crashing through "no man's land" at Guantanamo, where they might have been shot by U.S. Marines or Cuban soldiers. Distinctly suicidal as a bunch, one might wonder what common denominator they might have to cause them to do *two identical* social crimes, such as crash *out* through Guantanamo, and crash *back* via skyjack.

At the time of Sven's skyjack, he was an abject failure. He was running from an impulse to kill the officials who had taken a child from him, because of his inability to care for her.

## THE CASE OF ABE

Although I first interviewed the patient, at this point let us leave his description in the hands of Dr. Johnston, who sent me the following ward note some days after the first interview:

As you probably remember, that patient is a tall young bank robber we interviewed about one month ago, in the series of fifteen men who had robbed banks. He was the serendipitous find of the man who had wanted to, and almost did, commit a skyjacking. We found him to be a rather paranoid individual who was robbing banks, thinking he was Robin Hood. He had a long history of flying dreams, as well as dreams of falling and paralysis, as a child. We concluded that he had a very disturbed ear as well.

He has been getting along fairly well recently, except for trouble sleeping. I spoke with him, at length, on May 8, 1970, and, during our conversation, several interesting things were revealed.

He spoke with clenched jaw and ground out his words between his teeth, as though it required exceptional labor to speak. His hands were constantly in motion, as though to say that speech could not truly convey his feelings. His body was tight and he appeared as though he were trapped. He complained at length on the *'existential fate of man,'* and said that *'all free will had been stripped from him'* and others, except that he alone was truly aware of the magnitude and severity of the realization. *'I am trapped in time and it seems to be moving so slowly . . . it feels like molasses or something . . . I can't seem to move properly, in the physical continuum, and I feel trapped in the temporal one as well.'* He stopped talking and sat reflecting in silence for a bit. Breaking the silence, he slowly raised his arms in the position of flight. As he did so, he appeared happier, contented, in fact almost radiant. . . . *'I want to fly.'* Away from the prison? *'Not necessarily; being in an institution isn't so bad. I wish I was closer to home, so I could get visits. I just want to fly and feel better.'* Silence for a bit. *'I think, somehow, that I'm being punished or tortured.'* Tortured? *'Yeah, you know . . . this may sound funny, but I think I'm a person who is really different from others. . . . A god and I've had my memory taken away, and sent here to experience this horror.'* A god? Like Christ? *'Oh, hell no. Not like that. I'm not crazy. No, I mean like one of those Greek gods or characters from mythology. My memory has been taken away and I'm powerless to do anything, or able to get away. These bastards here* [inmates and staff] *won't leave me alone. . . . I can't get away they're eating me alive.'* Any Greek god in particular? Long pause. *'Prometheus.'*

## Comment

This case provides a bridge, through one man, between skyjackers, bank robbers, and men who wanted to skyjack but did not. He came so close. He wrote his note. He *stood up* in the aisle and was waiting there for the hostess when his companion pulled him down. The only thing that held him back was his love for his father, who was still living.

Of course, since the patient was never formally charged with the crime, it is obvious that nothing can be learned from the case, and especially not since there seems to be some connection between the deep equilibratory connections between skyjackers, bank robbers, and acid heads. He is a patient we particularly wanted to send to the Northwestern University Medical School for study.

## WONDERLAND

Speaking of madmen and delusions—It is appropriate to discuss the final governmental folly: the Presidential Task Force and its control systems. Public pressure on the FAA, for control of the problem, necessitated the creation of a special task force to reassure the airplane passenger that everything possible was being done. A group of laymen was assembled.

They were not allowed to examine the offenders. Such limited information as they had was put into a gigantic computer, which yielded five factors. These became the great national secret, formerly called a "personality profile." It is now more wisely called a "behavior profile," even though that is a misnomer.

Recently, a spokesman for the task force stated, in connection with the profile, that it *"would clear 99.5% of the passengers."* [1] How many people are involved each year in the other .5% of all airline passengers?

Anyone who has read the foregoing histories, can see that the surface manifestations here are highly variable, and cannot be reduced to five workable factors, which are quickly identifiable by untrained personnel.

The profile is true enough, *but it is a fraud.* Four offenders in this volume do not fit it, but are serving federal prison sentences, in connection with the crime. *Fully 25% (or more) of all successful skyjackers will not fit the profile.* Even when rigidly applied, the method cannot be as much as 75% effective. Even so, 27,000,000 passengers a year will become "suspects."

[1] Proceedings of meeting in Washington, D.C., of Airline Passenger Association, July 16, 1970.

Every male reading this volume fits one of the five characteristics of the profile, and could fit all of the other four, at the drop
of a hat, by traveling quickly and not following his usual habits
in the purchase of a ticket.

As to the magnetometer, opportunities arose to discuss it with
slightly over a half of the offenders in this series. Each one of them
quickly gave several ways to successfully evade that little piece of
trash. Unfortunately, some of the methods that came to their minds
were *far more potentially lethal* than the method they had originally
used.

Thus, we create an expensive police state, based on fallacious
assumptions. It will be tremendously expensive to create, even
more so to operate. It will be ineffective, and worse yet, will en-
gender mutation of the crime, which will sharply increase the overall risk to the airplane public.

But Congress gives these career employees no choice. They've
got to work within the permission they are allowed, even if, in the
process, they must lie to themselves, their superiors, and the public.

These same congressional attitudes tie the hands of the Department of State, in such a way that diplomacy is rendered impossible.

But you and I are damned fools if we expect a career man to
lay that career on the line by telling Congress the truth about itself
or its methods. Only a self-supporting person can safely "stand up"
to speak the facts. (The accuracy of that statement may well be
tested in coming months by what happens to my federal consul-
tancies.)

# XIII

## Psycho-Pathological Factors

### MURDER/RAPE/SUICIDE

At an early stage of this study, I was planning to write an article about skyjackers, and my notes reveal that I was going to use the term *murder/rape/suicide* in the form it appears here, an illustration suggesting common elements, even interchangeabilities among the three words. Such a form appears to be even more meaningful now than it did then. It is now clear that every man in the series was desperately driven toward one or another of these acts and that in the final analysis, each combined it with an ethical representative of his own "mysteries" into an act that, although a capital crime, was regarded by him as less than a sin.

I view a prohibition against murder/rape/suicide as a part of the basic social compact, as fundamental to the guarantees that every man must extend to every other man about him for the preservation of society. The *murderer,* through his act, completely severs his ties with *one* individual—his victim—and in so doing gives notice to the rest of humanity that he values them no differently and hence he has opted out of society. The *suicide,* by destroying himself, denies that his ties to anyone and everyone are important, and his act is in effect a statement that he has left society. The *rapist,* by the violent act committed on one of the opposite sex, severs his connections with others. On the one hand, he declares to all women that he no longer needs their approval; on the other

177

hand, he announces to all men, each of whom has his own woman (one of whom might have been his victim), that he fears none, he has contempt for all, and he has removed himself from society.

Each of these men grew to detest himself, because of events in his past. Failure after failure gradually aroused an intense hostility that was slowly transferred from himself to society in an attempt to defend himself against a rising desire to commit suicide. This hostility was not of a specific political coloration and had nothing whatsoever to do with political ideologies or comparable issues. It was simple and direct, devoted to the proposition that only through the deliberate destruction of someone, including the self, would it be possible to reconstitute pride. Even in the act of suicide, he would not be as powerless as in every other area of his life. It would be his action, not the consequence of some other individual's decision. In murder and rape, there would be a single, massive retaliation against a once emulated figure. It would be a victory over the self.

The response of the individual toward murder/rape/suicide should be viewed as his last societal response prior to his regressing to the earliest stage of his existence when the hostile emotion becomes a mirror image of the hostile aspect of gravity itself, and is cataclysmic and sub-human in character. In the act of skyjacking, he symbolically rapes, he threatens to murder, and he flirts with death (suicide). Consequently, he experiences all sides of this triad of violence, while he also flies. He has done it all! For one moment, all alone, he has achieved omnipotence, precisely because he has not done any of these things, except symbolically. He has, in fact, restrained, i.e., triumphed over, all four drives. He had neither killed, nor raped, neither killed himself, nor flown.

Each man in this series (with one exception)[1] had a better,

---

[1] It was George, who did not do his "own thing." The act was Gladys' tool, who thought she could see what his "thing" should have been, and he allowed himself to be led. It does no good to act out someone else's symbolism, or even our own, if it is not at that moment dictated by a part of ourselves which demands *this* expression *now*. Had he been up to or driven to the act by coordination of his own needs and symbols, his would have been a different story.

more tolerable body image and self-image *after* the crime that he had before. Why? The answer is simple: He acquired dignity. Had he committed the crime (murder/rape/suicide) toward which he was powerfully driven, he would have indulged in the ultimate withdrawal into the self, but in his ability to act alone bravely in the face of clear danger and to commit a secular crime, he affirmed that he belonged to the human race.

I was reminded of the case of Rafe, the skyjacker strongly driven toward raping his fifteen-year-old daughter, who said, "As the feeling rose to a maddening pitch, one thought was that I could leave home—go north—and that it would all die down. *But I could come back from there. The only way I could not come back was to go south.*" The action of skyjacking was perfectly chosen as the one way (other than to kill self or to kill her) by means of which to achieve victory over the self. It would put the self where it could not come back. Another comment he made upon hearing about the consequences of the rape of a little girl: "Thank you for what you have told me. If that could have been the result on my own daughter, then this whole damned thing was worthwhile." In a sense, his feelings were shared by every man in the sample. Had he, in the commission of this crime, managed to hold on to his selfhood, then any punishment would have been tolerable, because *he would be able to live (or die) with himself*. In every instance, effecting the basic drive would have been "hell." By "hell," I mean each man's particular version of each, for each felt that the act he was being driven to perform was so drastic that he would never have had the capacity to establish a permanent level at which he could rid himself of the horrible sense of "begining to fall"—which is called guilt.

On the other hand, these men were able to adapt to their remorse over the results of their skyjacking and still experience elation. To put it simply, the *bad circumstances* in which they found themselves after the crime *had a bottom*. What was unpleasant was set forth by law, and no matter what it was, it was at least specific and limited (even the death penalty belongs here). Thus, most of their input after the skyjackings served to reaffirm their existence, their being, and their worth, because they were bathed in their own approval of what they did not do.[2]

To reach a deeper level, let us forget for the moment that man's sensory-emotional system is lubricated in a changing chemical-hormonal sea, and let us pretend that the psyche has nothing to contend with but its own self. In this view, the personality is nothing but a series of electrochemical inputs derived from experience, in which a sort of balance or proportion exists whereby one is able to evaluate his own self by a system of negative and positive criteria. If, after years of inadequate and misguided effort, these men had steadily depleted their sense of worth, until in a last desperate moment they plunged into this symbolic action in which they saw themselves more or less permanently as men who had done *one* fine thing, then their new inputs could have had only one consequence, —namely, a gradual sense of rising from that which was lowest within them. Even though some depression regarding the consequences might be evident, their continuing new experience would be that of elation. Their depression would be related to the past, but the present would produce a sense of elation. They would, therefore, be both "up" and "down" at the same moment, yet the overall direction would aways be upward. The moment in which they acted in response to all of the stimuli responsible for their act, was the one in which they reached the absolute bottom.

Now, let me clearly state that it does not appear relevant whether the men here were or were not sane, as measured by the legal tests for sanity. What is relevant is that in every instance each was forced to move by an irresistible impulse, and that, in addition, in their acts of individual, if foolish, heroics, each reaffirmed his essential humanity.[3]

[2] A serious student of this behavior will read the classical work by Karl Menninger, *et al., The Vital Balance* (Viking Press: New York, N. Y., 1963), in which his own description of deteriorating behavior beautifully illustrates the process described above. In addition he includes the work of his brother William Menninger from World War II in which the prevalent psychiatric battle casualty called combat exhaustion is fully described. It is interesting how individuals in my study so closely parallel combat exhaustion. Could a cold war and civil unrest also produce battle casualties?

[3] This volume had just reached the galley stage at the time of the recent Palestinian outrages, as I left for Russia. While there, and shortly after my

If a man can be considered to be potentially depletable by continuing failure, these men surely were. Real success and a real sense of honor always seemed just beyond reach. At least, in a single moment, each performed the act of standing on his own two feet. Whether the outcome was success or failure from our point of view, in every instance it was a victory for them.

From the physiological point of view, the chemistry of guilt is different from that of depression. Guilt anticipates pain and is more closely related to the first phase of stress reaction in which fear, with its acceleratory action, is evident. Depression, on the other hand, is psychic pain and reflects the sustained consequence of the altered physiology that results from sustained stress. The threat of stress, like other anticipations, may be momentarily exultant in character. We play all sorts of games in which this is the physiological state we seek. Let us assume, for the moment, that the physiology of success is markedly different from the physiology of failure, that the chemistry of mania is a polar extreme of the physiology of despair. The occurrence of stress is not anticipatory, because it does not lie in the future. In fact, it so fully fills the present as to preclude the possibil-

---

return, I presented this data to very well-trained psychoanalytic groups. It was interesting to see how slow we are to learn and how vigorously we cling to our fixed ideas. After finishing my presentation, and while the group was still visibly shaken by the knowledge that single offenders manifested common factors, hence providing a possible basis for control, the group members all said: "But, of course, the Palestinian thing is purely political."

This is biased thinking and a denial of scientific method. Quite simply, we can't know about the Palestinian form until it is studied. At this stage of the game I can argue (with a great deal of fact on my side) that the Palestinian form possibly involves the same emotional factors as those in my study. First, the phenomenon *occurred at a hostile border* in which that factor was critical. Second, the Palestinians (as a group) found themselves at a *terminal moment of failure,* exactly like that of my single offenders, at the moment Israel and Egypt began to negotiate. Third, after the event, all the quotations of the offenders were strikingly similar to statements made by the offenders in this series, *i.e.,* "We knew we were doomed *unless we stood up* and attracted world attention." Fourth, the present series demonstrates that *groups can act in concert* with all members responding to the same stimulus. (Do not overlook the fact that there are two groups in my series.) Fifth, even with my limited information about these Palestinian offenders, *there are suggestive facts* known about the lives of some of them. Sixth, neither political affiliation nor an army uniform *are proof of sanity,* particularly not in a volunteer army threatened with extinction. The argument I always hear is a simple one: "Well, *I always think of skyjacking as political."*

ity of a future, wiping out anticipatory possibilities. Caught in stress, one hurts, and physiology continues to guard oneself and prepare for more of the same, until at last one's stressful capacity is exceeded, at which point one falls in defeat. The exhausted adrenocortical response found in many chronic depressive individuals is a good example of this state. The person has simply fought stress until permanently overwhelmed. Now, we know there are many other highly vascular structures (mainly endocrine) which have a part in this response and which alter under tremendous affective onslaught.

As readily as I accept all of the above, however, it is only with real difficulty that I can perceive precisely how an affective disorder can maintain itself in such an almost unaltered state from day to day and be strictly psychic in origin. In sleep, the greater part of the night is spent in relative relaxation even though dreams do seem to occur at moments in which activity heightens. It has, however, always seemed to me that in both the psychic and the physiologic realms these periods of relative rest and inactivity should be adequate for the "soul" to heal itself. This seems particularly true when I consider the high level of vascularity of the hormonal system, and if I view a brain cell as a fixed resonator. The fixity of the direction or clinical course of affective disorders is made easier to understand if one concedes the effect of both psychic and physiologic factors, but then moves one step further and adds a *purely physical* factor, whose nature is perhaps so fixed that the relaxatory, healing capacities of sleep do not repair it. Thus, one might wake up in a somewhat healed psychic and physiologic state, only to be thrown once again into the maelstrom by the unaltered physical component of the complex reaction.

For the moment, let us assume that three factors operate in the seriously depressed individual: the psychic, the physiologic, and the physical. I am absolutely convinced that there was a specific reason why the skyjackers chose that particular crime in preference to all others as a means of achieving their purpose. The suicide-driven among them could have held up a bank with an unloaded gun, as so many others do, and succeeded in drawing fire which they could not have returned. The murder-driven could have murdered or "accidentally" wiped themselves out in a car wreck. The rape-driven could have had their victim or managed their destruction in some way. Yet, they did not, none of them. They all committed a crime in which the physical sensations connected with it involved an upward movement of their physical body at precisely the same time when they experienced the social sensations accruing from it. For them, the upward physical sensation was precisely correlative with the symbolic content of their personal development.

It appears incontrovertible to me that it was imperative for them to simultaneously defy the reality of their social environment and the reality of their physical environment (gravity). As if by the act of defying both *in the service of an ultimate ethic,* they were able to effect a concurrent body- and self-image and reverse the downward plunge of their existence. Thus, the two realities were re-wedded into an affectively more comfortable state, regardless of the legal outcome. As men and as human beings, they "pulled themselves together."

What I propose here is that there comes a moment in the lives of all defeated persons when the unpleasantness of reality, and their psychic and physiologic response to it, becomes at last unbearable. This may occur in or out of the condition of "legal sanity." If one is out, he still feels pain and is still capable of falling even further into himself, since apparently even his delusions do not hold him up. At this moment, those who have the capacity to respond to the symbolic content of the action, perform one desperate act calculated to overcome that fixed physical factor that prevents sleep from restoring their beings. It is a gamble by means of which a last attempt is made at affirming their own selfhoods and the world. More precisely, it is a recapitulation of that moment in which they first stood on their own feet and attempted to walk.

In this respect, it is most important that the reader remember that in four cases the first conscious memory was specifically related to the assumption of the vertical axis. Out of twenty random individuals, the chances of the earliest memory of four being related to their first steps are surely astronomical. It is also most relevant that this occurred in a group where the consistent repetitive dream from childhood was one of paralysis and where a rare crime involving flight was the common denominator.

When pushed downward by the ever increasing effects of his own personal failure, or by the caprice of happenstance, the skyjacker moves psychically and physically closer and closer to the time when his regression carries him into the psycho-physio-physical state associated with the period prior to the assumption of the vertical posture. The farther he moves toward that state, the more he becomes conscious of and threatened by the emergence of that part of the murder/rape/suicide aspect of primal rage which best fits his particular psychic and situational determinants. His action is designed to subvert that final goal, and in most cases it succeeds.

## THE PARENTAL CAUSE

There emerged a distinct image of parents of skyjackers, together with an image of family interaction and dynamics. First, the father was violent and probably an alcoholic; second, the mother was religious and probably a zealot.

With few exceptions, as, for example, in the case of Bob, where the father's violence was limited largely to destructive verbosity, in the case of Sam, whose father was described as "loving, but Germanic," and the case of Dick, whose father was absent during his first eleven years, the picture is a consistent one.

In Bob's case, the father was always nagging his wife, but no physical violence appears to have been present. The mother's religious stance was not as exaggerated as that of the other mothers. With Bob, two factors of some importance may have been operating. In the first place, he lived in an area where identification with the space program was easily and readily available. In the second place, probably more than any of the others, Bob consciously expressed identification with the astronauts through his compulsive tendency to collect their memorabilia. It may be of importance also that Bob, like Sam, consciously planned violence against his future host, Castro. (The men with the physically least violent fathers seemed to entertain the notion of killing Castro rather than those with more violent fathers.)

In Sam's case, the father was apparently the most loving one in the group, although the reference to his Germanic origin might well be a screen for repressed memories. The mother, what with her Baptist faith and her grief over her lost child with its religious overtones, reinforced by the religious orientation of the grandparents, certainly lived up to the image of the zealot.

As might have been expected, the partial exception noted in Sam's case (the paternal image) shows more clearly than do any of the others what the common basic picture might have been. It was clearly stated that the pervading moral tone was set by the mother, but its reinforcement was left to the father. The constructed image looked like this:

Father = Discipline Without Authority = Force
Mother = Authority Without Responsibility = Virtue

If one carries the situation of *paternal force without virtue* and *maternal virtue without force* back to the other cases, many factors tend to fall into place.

In Dick's case, there was no father, although the grandmother was a fit substitute. The description of her did not noticeably differ from that of other fathers. The image of the mother, who vacillated between alcoholism and virtue, was unusual, too. Dick did not skyjack. He was powerfully driven to do so immediately following Apollo VIII; he flew twice, with a gun on his person, each time determined to perform the act, and his history of violence and gun usage was much more in keeping with his plan than could be said of the others, yet he was unable to act, because he was not angry with his father, or his uncle, or his son. The males in his life were fit for his love, and the final moment of crisis pivoted on the fact that he was unable to be unpatriotic as it were: his "pater" had been adequate to his needs, and he could not leave his fatherland even though he was being pursued for his other offenses.

The father's image, on the whole, closely approximates the perceived nature of the gravitational force. It is violent, inevitable, instantaneous, and unmerciful. It is indifferent and final, and by its very physical nature stands in stark contrast to that of the mother who appears as transcendent, ethereal, pure, concerned, and human, but powerless. Her image is without "heft" or physical quality; she is a poor, weak, helpless person wishing and longing eternally for a world where her ethics of love, concern, and goodwill could be freely exercised, but she is condemned to live in a world where a physical reality (the father) is holding her and her children down in eternal subjection.

In almost every instance, the maternal figure used the son as a wailing wall to whom she confided her grief over the existence of the physical father. She taught the son to admire and respect the beauty of her aspirations and to loathe the uninspired physical force of the father. Opposing systems, perhaps basic to man, stare uncomprehendingly across a bottomless chasm in the structure of such marriages. Neither system admires or respects the other, and the child is offered no compromise between them. The barrier between the parents is a hostile one, and the child must clearly stand on one side or the other. When he stands on one side, he must completely abjure all connection with the other. This hostile barrier is quite important to the issue of skyjacking. In this crime, with the exception of a few very confused episodes, there is a condition of hostility between the nation from which the plane is stolen and the nation to which it is directed. Consider what the history of skyjacking would have been if the first offenders had gone to Canada. They would have been sent back. That would have ended the whole matter.

Among children whose parents have maintained fixed hostile barriers between themselves, there is usually a great deal of back-and-forth movement as the child becomes a traitor to one and then to the other by "taking sides." At such moments, when the child sides first with one and with the other, he achieves a "king's X" on the rejected parent.

It is interesting to observe the extraordinary rate of frequency with which the fathers vanished by death, desertion, or divorce.

Brian—Father had a coronary a year before the crime.
Elmer—Father died seven years before the crime.

Bob—Father alive and home, but lost all ambition and was semi-retired for four years before the crime.

Mark—Father deserted family when Mark was nine.

Oscar—Father deserted family when Oscar was eight.

Ronald—Grandfather (who took father's place) died when Ronald was nineteen. Father alive and home, and Ronald had conscious murderous feelings toward him.

Gladys—Father alive, but he divorced the mother when Gladys was fifteen.

George—Father alive, but "whipped by life."

Ted—Father alive (possibly divorced).

Will—Father died when Will was twenty-four.

Rafe—Father died when Rafe was twenty-two.

Dan—Father deserted family when Dan was ten.

Frank—Father died when Frank was twenty-two.

Sam—Father alive and in good health. Mother semi-invalid.

Dick—Father died of a coronary when Dick was thirteen.

Philip—Father divorced mother over religion.

Only in three cases were the fathers alive and home at the time of the crime, and in good health. It ought to be noted that Bob and Ronald had clear plans to assassinate Castro. In all other cases, the fathers were just out of the picture. The sharpness of this detail is most striking.

A very interesting factor is that the mothers who were deserted, divorced, or widowed did not remarry, except for Dick's. It seems fair to say either that their ability to deal with marriage was limited, or that their failure to remarry reflects the consequences of the violence they endured in their first marriage.

As a rule, the families tended to pull together against the fathers as long as they were in the home. After they were gone, the families closed the gap around the focus of an older child and did not open up to take in a new father figure.

Where there was divorce or separation, the children never went with the father and did not join him later, as is often the case in adolescents. After divorces, the fathers were simply out of the picture.

It is my overall thesis that these men introjected the fearful image of a father at an early age, a father who would "do them in

if they dared to rise and try to act like men," and that this image
of the impossible father had an intimate connection with the son's
gravito-inertial experiences and his definition of the impossible, revealing an important determinant of a crime specifically involving
flight. The son would not "dream" of flying or of raping with the
father still alive and at home, except when the murderous intent
was sheathed in patriotism and transferred to Castro. The absence
of the father lessened inhibitions; as with Prometheus, once the god
had turned away, he could act.

## SEXUAL ELEMENTS

The unusual shyness, timidity, and sexual passivity of the men
stood out even in the first interview. Actually, such behavior is not
unexpected in the context of the angry, possessive, and abusive
sexuality of the father. Boys raised in such families would come to
be ashamed of the existence of sexual feelings in their own bodies
when they realized their mother's humiliated reactions to the rape-
like character of the paternal sexuality. It is likely that the highly
religious (and probably frigid) mothers were frequently assaulted
more or less publicly by the drunken husbands who were forced
into proctracted, involuntary celibacy. Not infrequently, such men
would force their wives into a public sexual act or its symbolic
equivalent. In Elmer's family, just such an episode led to the
father's being stabbed in the back by an older son. Less dramatic
but similar events came to light in subsequent cases.

An additional reinforcing factor emerged when it became obvious that mothers turned to their children regularly and in a semi-
seductive fashion for the love they wanted and for the allies they
needed. In interview after interview, I heard statements like these:
"When she was really upset she'd take all of us kids in the car and
drive and talk about the old man," or "She always turned to me
when he hurt her and I was supposed to make it all right." It became apparent that as soon as a child was old enough to be verbal

as well as capable of any sort of ethical stand, both the mother and the father proselytized him as an ally. The fathers made their pitch on the simple logic that a boy's loyalty belonged to the father. By the same token, it can be safely assumed that if the son failed to be loyal, he was judged to be non-masculine.

The appeal of the mothers lay in the loftiness of their aspirations. It was enhanced by the belief that their values were derived from a higher and more powerful Father. The boys evidently got a great deal of instruction from the mothers that consisted of negative criticism of the fathers and positive instruction to emulate the example of the mother whose goodness could be expected, in spite of the travail of this world, to lift her to that higher realm.

It is evident how all these factors would affect the Oedipal situation. The mother being in direct competition for the allegiance of the son would be seductive. The moments of "togetherness" with her would be intensely stimulating for sexual fantasies, both because of the closeness and because of the rejection of the father implied by his replacement by the son. Such a situation is strongly conducive to introducing a great deal of guilt. At such times, the presence of an idealized desexualized figure who could be loved *safely* by the mother could be a welcome identification for the boy.

Early in the study, I discerned a pattern of the presence of younger sisters toward whom, as an extension of the "sympathy for mother" motif, they had been instructed to be protective and "honorable." On the other hand, not infrequently they were "used sexually" by female relatives, neighbors, and family friends.

I consistently ran into interesting responses to questions regarding younger sisters. The men generally mentioned their births or existence, but always in an offhand way. When I pressed for more information in an attempt to assess their relationship, their response was evasive or tangential, so that our discussion veered off. When I pressed a little harder, the response was that sister was "usually with mother" or "We just weren't bent that way" (not sexually curious). When I persisted, I usually encountered a rigid and powerful resistance, like that of one subject who told me that he could "talk of other things," but this area represented a "closed door beyond which lay the privacy of other people still living," and the interview would end right there if I did not relent. They had no trouble referring to other female relatives or to other women because the guilt of aggression was absent.

This was the *only area in any interview* where the men dared to pit their strength *man to man.* Even in areas where full disclosure could have affected the duration of their imprisonment, if I had revealed it to the legal authorities, they did not hold back. Each appeared to have accepted me for what I was, a physician studying a disease process. Therefore, they trustingly made a full disclosure in spite of possible embarrassment or legal complication. *But,* and this seems quite important, in the area of younger sisters, their ego organization would falter and fail time after time, which leads me to suggest that these sisters might have represented a more conscious target of emergent sexuality and hostility than had the mother. There may not have been any overt expression of such feelings, but the evidence for fearful fantasies and wishes is weighty.

If the unusual parental conflicts coupled with fights for allegiance produced a situation where a boy might well have developed fears of his masculinity, how strongly reinforced is the situation by a little sister whose sexual curiosity matures at about the same rate as his own? How much would the frigid mother be aware of and opposed to this emergent interest? How often would she use the sister as a "case in point" through which to instruct the boy as to the impropriety of aggressive behavior? The reinforced experience would be undoubtedly much more powerful, and it seems to have been so from the available data.

Although these men were geared to disrupt an interview to avoid any discussion of little sister, they were eager to discuss their early sexual experiences if they could recall any. Without exception, these were episodes with older girls from two to twenty years their senior.

The girls were always the aggressors. A typical example was one in which the boy was six and the girl nine. Often, such relationships continued up to the time of menstruation, when the boys were usually left out in the cold. They could not turn to girls their own age or younger, because they were too passive.

The older girls were never older sisters, but usually older sisters of other boys. Often, older sisters "traded off" little brothers as an extension of their sexual interest in him and out of curiosity about their girl friend. Both interests were thus simultaneously gratified. In liaisons between older girls (nine) and younger boys (six) there was usually an attempt at intercourse, whereas in liaisons between older boys (eight) and younger girls (five-six) activity was usually limited to looking.

The older girl syndrome was part of the developmental picture of almost every skyjacker, and led them directly to what was to become generally passive orientation. They did not mind waiting for a girl to make the move, because they knew from experience that she would. Active and aggressive boys do not have this experience, because they have never waited. Those men who later became sexually active with multiple partners invariably used paid prostitutes. Dealing with whores did not require the ego orientation necessary for maintaining an aggressive stance whereby the resistance of a partner is met and dealt with.

Where marriage was entered into, the chosen partner tended to dominate the man, and it was usually she who seduced him first and proposed later. Almost without exception, the men were reviled by their wives, strove to placate them, and were often cuckolded. When this occurred, the women did not adopt a guilt-ridden attitude assumed by straying wives of more masculine men. As a rule, one of these wives angrily confronted the husband with a statement that he had "never pleased her sexually, had a tiny penis, and not the least idea in the world about what to do with it." The husbands, in turn, were shattered by disbelief and paralyzed, rather than angry and prone to act out either by a beating or by getting another woman to prove their "manhood."

Thus, the childhood of each of these men was characterized by a situation in which the father molested the mother, and the mother bemoaned the fact to the son. The son may have longed for little sister after the manner of his father, but he set himself up as the victim of the aggressions of older girls. In a sense, both he and mother were helpless subjects of rape.

It is not difficult to discern the delight they must have experienced when they approached little sister-mother stewardess, gun in hand, and said, "Honey, we're going all the way—to Cuba," and the sense of power they derived from making daddy (flying the plane) stay put, making him permit the abuse of sister-mother, and forcing him to perform the bidding of sonny.

For these men, to command a woman or even to attempt it approaches the outer limits of imagination. It follows that whenever a stewardess was spunky or scared enough to say, "Don't you point that thing at me," the gun was obediently pointed in another direction. In one instance, the stewardess slammed the cockpit door in the face of a desperate skyjacker, whereupon he quietly returned to his seat, put the shotgun down, and waited for the plane to land.

## THE SENSE OF FAILURE

The chart on page 193 depicts the situation of each skyjacker at the time of his crime. We have seen that each was willing to die during the act or as a consequence of it. I did not consider them to be suicidal unless self-destruction was consciously contemplated. Creating a situation where the consequences were unpredictable was not regarded as evidence of suicidal intent. Thus, all could be viewed as being unconsciously motivated toward suicide, and some as consciously motivated. Unconscious intent must not be overlooked in connection with the possibility of death penalty. Only the sixteen cases which are fully described, are included in these graphs.

During the three-month period preceding his crime each skyjacker touched the highest level of accomplishment he has ever attained. Only one (Ted) has achieved a reasonable level of financial success through his own efforts for any length of time. Sam alone was employed at the time of his crime, but even here family connection was involved. Aside from Ted and Sam, earning potential was markedly limited for all, because of poor achievement.

| | Highest Accomplishment Level | Status Level at Time of Skyjack | Principal Conscious Drive | Principal Conscious Target |
|---|---|---|---|---|
| Brian | School teacher | Fired | Suicide | Self |
| Elmer | Factory employee | Fired | Murder | Boss/wife |
| Bob | Student | Dropout | Murder | Father/Castro |
| Dick | Unemployed | On the run | Mass murder | Police |
| Mark | Petty thief | On the run | Murder/suicide | Police/Self |
| Oscar | Hospital patient | Unemployed | Mass murder | State legislature Hospital staff |
| Philip | Aircraft mechanic | Fired | Suicide/murder | Self/wife |
| Ronald | Store manager | Fired | Murder | Father |
| Sam | Straw boss in father's business | ? | Suicide/murder | Son/Castro/father? |
| Gladys | Student | Unemployed | Murder | Father or mass |
| George | Student | Unemployed | Murder | Mass or chance |
| Ted | Entrepreneur | On the run | Murder/suicide | F.B.I./self |
| Will | Forger | Arrested | Suicide | Self |
| Rafe | Public relations | Failed | Rape | Daughter |
| Dan | Army private | Unemployed | Murder | Mother/chance |
| Frank | Bank robber | On the run | Murder | Self |

*Occupational Status at Time of Skyjack Summary*

| | |
|---|---|
| Fired | 4 |
| Unemployed | 4 |
| On the run | 3 |
| Arrested | 1 |
| Dropout | 1 |
| Failure | 1 |
| Unclassifiable but employed | 1 |

Except for Sam, not one individual in the group knew when he arose in the morning that his services were necessary or that someone was counting on him to be at work that day. In each, a shameful sense of uselessness was consistently manifest.

*Principal Conscious Hostile Drive Summary*

| | |
|---|---|
| Family member | 8 |
| Self | 8 |
| Police | 3 |
| Mass | 3 |
| Castro | 2, |
| Boss | 1 |
| ? | 1 |

It will be observed that sixteen individuals had twenty-six primary conscious targets, which is accounted for by those who had double targets. If one were to include the wide range of other possible unconscious targets, the number would rise even more sharply.

The precipitating event from a situational point of view for any given subject was that for the first and only time he was confronted with his particular situation. One way or another, by a series of manipulations, rationalizations, or symbol formations, these men had managed always to escape a "first" experience with the sensation of total failure. Now, they were confronted with a situation from which they could not escape. Here, an intriguing paradox would seem to emerge in that the act they performed was dramatically at variance with their previous non-violent solutions and consequently appears to be "a first." But this would be true only if one used the yardstick of their adult behavior, and not if one viewed their whole lives. In effect, "the flight" was a re-enactment of their previous resolution of the Oedipal conflict, in which they crossed the hostile barrier between father and mother, disowning, in the process, identification with and murderous impulses toward the father.

One might say that their original and basic fear of failure consisted in their inability either to identify successfully with the violent father or to defeat him physically. They fled from that failure by means of identification with the mother, becoming non-genital, spiritual figures in the process.

# XIV
## Control Group Studies

One would conclude from the foregoing that these men constitute a significant variation from society at large. But conclusions require verification, even if it be as crude as the evidence in this chapter. Interviews with bank robbers had already suggested similarities to the skyjackers.

Lacking research data that would have been appropriate sources of norms for comparison with salient data from this study, six control groups were set up, following the kind advice of Dr. Karl Menninger.

### GROUP I

This first group was composed of so-called average businessmen, who had offices in the building in which I was working. Qualifications for this group were frequent travel by plane and at least three national credit cards per member.

The premise was that most were very like the businessmen who occasionally sit beside a skyjacker on a plane. In addition, this group was assumed to be significantly different from our skyjackers.

## GROUP II

This group consisted of fifteen airline pilots, any one of whom might some day find himself looking down the barrel of a sky-jacker's gun.

This group, too, was assumed to display significant differences from the skyjackers.

## GROUP III

This group was composed of fifteen ministers, half of them from my regular Episcopal seminar. This might be criticized on the grounds that it employed a selection principle, since the meeting is attended by ministers who would like to understand a little more about the emotional problems of their parishioners. The other half of it was a purely random sample from the Methodist faith, each of whom accepted interview without the slightest knowledge of what was involved.

We assumed differences from skyjackers here too.

## GROUP IV

This group was made up of fifteen convicted bank robbers. The following characteristics of this group hinted at probable similar-ities to our skyjacker group: (1) Eighty-eight percent of the bank robbers, like the skyjackers, had no criminal record that involved the use of weapons—indeed, they had no criminal record at all. (2) Many of them had committed their crime between age twenty and age thirty, while experiencing acute periods of social failure not unlike that of our skyjacker sample. (3) The gun carried at the time of the crime was often unloaded, even though each was going into an area he knew to be protected by armed guards whose duty it was to shoot him when he displayed his weapon. Many had *no* weapon at all, but used only a note. This finding was compatible with the tremendous incidence of conscious and unconscious suicidal motivation seen among skyjackers.

We expected close similarities in the crypto-vestibular[1] symptoms, *but not in family structure.*

## GROUP V

This group contained fifteen young LSD users, most of whom were also convicted of various armed thefts.

We anticipated a mixed bag of psychopathology here, and a basic crypto-vestibular similarity to skyjackers and bank robbers.

## GROUP VI

This group was made up of random convicts, the individual nature of whose crimes may possibly be described as a "crazy act" in which violent, anti-social, and unreality factors were clearly manifest. There was, for example, a man who killed ten little girls and four women, and also a leader of an ethnic revolt who was prepared to begin a civil war to gain proper rights for his people. This group is incomplete, with only five members.

We hoped to pinpoint a crypto-vestibular similarity here, too.

## COMMENTS BEFORE FINDINGS

Many of the skyjackers wanted to be successful businessmen, commercial flyers, bank robbers, revolutionaries, murderers, ministers, or drug users. Many of them have made attempts of one kind or another to achieve distinction of this sort. In fact, the general population of skyjackers included three ministers, ten student pilots, five LSD users, two businessmen, and two bank robbers.

[1] The meaning of this usage is set forth in Appendix A.

I would like to point out that the evaluation of findings does not go beyond the interview data, and only slight correlation of other psychological tests has been undertaken, owing to pressures of time, funds, etc. I nevertheless have a high degree of confidence in the conclusions drawn from the interview data.

The groups were evaluated largely on the basis of two factors: (1) the frequency of the characteristic hostile family border, between the parents, accompanied by the desexualizing consequences, and (2) the early memories, dreams, and physical activities which appeared to be unusually frequent among skyjackers.

# FINDINGS

## Group I—Business Men

These men were a colorless collection, as compared with the skyjackers, by the above criteria.

There was absolutely no relationship involving family structure. The men came from all kinds of homes, but none had clear similarities to the pervading skyjacker pictures.

None experienced adult dreams of paralysis or flight, and only a few had dreamed of either as children. Evidence of peregrination, neurotic interest in flight or space were not detected. There were no psychoses or hospitalizations.

Conclusion: Unrelated to the specimen.

## Group II—Pilots

Pilots came from bilaterally religious homes, characterized by stability and hard work. Parents were invariably close to each other.

Pilots had so little neurotic involvement in flight that none of them ever paid a cent for flying lessons. They all waited until after college, and when faced with the draft, decided in favor of the Air Force as a means to an end to avoid the infantry. They all reacted in a violent, negative way to the thought of parachutes.

"Cold-blooded" is not an unfair description of their lack of interpersonal investment in their loved ones, their excessive preoccupation with concrete "things" and with financial security.

Pilots were stay-at-home types. They rarely walked or drove cars and never paced. They had been good athletes. All were married and none cuckolded as far as they knew. Highly significant was the fact that only one had ever dreamed of flight as a child. That one man had one such dream. In that dream he was seated on a board, which acted as a wing.

Interestingly, pilots tended to cling to the left border of their Bender-Gestalt tests, according to a blind study graciously done for me by Dr. Bender. Could this be ocnophilia? Are the philobats private pilots?

The most promising possibility raised by this group has to do with whether there is a relationship between men with mild cryptovestibular involvement, who have failed in military flight training or just slid through, and our aviation accidents that are labeled "pilot error."

Pilots live dramatically different lives than do their pastoral brothers. They wear a uniform which distinctly signals their masculine role. They are often away from home, family, and identity. Their female associates are young, and as attractive as the company can hire. Their principal job concern is quite concrete, dealing with weather, schedules, mechanical and mathematical concerns. They have little need to deal with passengers and their problems, because of the buffer the stewardesses create between crew and passengers. Even on the ground, they need not fraternize with the traveling public. They constitute a small masculine society, moving through the crowd anonymously, powerfully.

Conclusion: Diametric opposites to skyjackers.

## Group III—Ministers

Ministers, like businessmen and pilots, come from all sorts of families, but not like those of skyjackers. They did offer a fairly frequent earliest memory of life, however, in which they were huddled in a box or some other warm, safe place, with a clear awareness of "the cold outside."

The "heavy existential despair" which had first appeared in three skyjacker "ministers" was replicated among a number of real ministers, which raises some curious questions about their choice of vocation and their automatic attitude selection. This area also offers interesting possibilities. In this connection, there were *soft* vestibular signs such as occasional flight dreams, interest in learning to fly, walking, and pacing.

Among ministers, dress is largely optional, and insignia of rank and quasi-military power are lacking. Most parishes would not tolerate frequent absences by their pastor, other than to visit regional church meetings where his identity clings to his coattails. His female associates are older, matronly, and far more reserved (although far from less involved). The concern of the minister is not expected to focus on the secular realm, but rather on a highly constant extra-terrestrial atmosphere. He follows absolute rules that leave no room for improvisation, and he is permitted no opportunities for mechanical toys. He is expected to be extremely responsive to the affective needs of all who call upon him, and no personal services of any other person will act as a buffer between himself and his flock. He generally moves singly through the crowd in the course of his daily rounds.

Conclusion: No similarity to family structure. Very mild vestibular signs.

## Ministers and Pilots

If the choice of the wife of the average airline pilot (in terms of beauty, ability to dress, and poise) were copied by the average minister, it would lead to an immediate gathering of the elders. They would not feel they could trust a man who wanted such a lovely, feminine partner. (The mind of such a fellow must surely be devoted to the wrong ideas.) Divorce has no effect at all on a pilot's career development, whereas a minister's ability to keep his job and chosen profession lies, frequently, in the hands of his wife, who may be well adapted to it, or may respond by abusing him or whipping herself.

A pilot's income runs from three to eight times that of his pastoral brother, whose Volkswagen bears no resemblance to the pilot's Jaguar or custom-rebuilt classic T-bird. Talk about birds of a different feather!

### Group IV—Bank Robbers

As expected, the skyjacker's closest kinsman is the bank robber, particularly in regard to his acute failure and his descent toward psychoses, which appear, as among skyjackers, to be related to his crypto-vestibular difficulties. On the other hand, his familial situation and his resolution of Oedipal conflicts are unrelated. He was often Daddy's favorite and considered him a friend. There was no hostile religious border between the parents, and bully big brothers and virginal sisters were scarce.

Simply put, the bank robber has an "unbalanced ear," but he was a spoiled kid (and Daddy's joy) from a very large, poor family. As likely as not, he was an angry foot-stomper when displeased. This was a *most* notable factor. It is quite unusual and unsettling to talk with a series of chronologically mature men and watch them stomp their feet at you when they are aroused by small displeasures. Their tone of voice at such moments, with the strident tone of a demanding four-year-old in it, is curious if one considers the "demand" of their crime. Their rate of overt homosexuality is startlingly high as compared with its overt absence among skyjackers.

Not infrequently, the timing of a given bank robbery was related to space events. One patient, who had been without a job for months prior to Apollo VIII, had a job handing out throwaway advertisements on the day of the moon walk. As the patient walked along the street listening to the event on his portable radio, he contrasted his own anonymous, unwanted position with that of Neil Armstrong. Four days later, as he stepped into a bank to rob it, he said to himself, "This is *my* space walk." This finding was no surprise, since we had already noticed this temporal relationship several times.

In addition to flying and paralytic dreams, the bank robber adds his own secret repetitive dream. As a child, he often dreamed of "having money" in his pockets or under his pillow. The dreams were so real he would waken and get out of bed *to check their reality*. His earliest memories were usually of gift objects or of "someone's giving him money."

## Group V—Acid Heads

This group too was unlike that of the skyjacker in family dynamics. They were less frequently psychotic, but had fairly similar (although softer) signs of crypto-vestibular disturbance. Of real interest to me was their lack of an ethical system with which to contain their "sense of the mysteries." They had absolutely no mythical religious base. They had received no formal religious training, and were in fact the children of forty-year-old, God-is-dead-generation-parents who had rebelled against the fundamentalism of the grandparents. As such, it was most dramatic to observe them wheeling about in space in search of "highs," "lows," "trips," and "space-outs" through drugs while at the same time becoming avid students of the Hindu religion. They simply "can't find their bearings" personally, professionally, socially, or religiously. Further study here could be *most* illuminating in regard to the relationship between love and a guiding principle of personal orientation

## Group VI—Mixed Offenders

The individuals in this group were actively disturbed in the crypto-vestibular area and gave clear evidence that their chief anti-social activity was sometimes stimulated and sometimes curbed by events in space. The evidence suggests that their sense of reality was touched by the incredibility of the event.

One militant political figure was most active over the period of the space program (1961–68). He was in prison during Apollo X.

He said, "When Armstrong stepped on the moon, he changed my whole life. In an instant I could see, from out there, the foolishness of our petty squabbles over land and 'race.' We are all one kind against the universe! I am through with my old cause. Now I am out to unite all men. . . ." Beyond this point he lapsed conversationally into the speed of light and the fourth dimension. *But his basic social orientation appears to have been changed by the news.* We found this most curious response to have been made repeatedly.

It seems quite probable that we will continue to find crypto-vestibular conditions among the group. Their family dynamics do not match those of the skyjacker.


## CONCLUSIONS FROM CONTROL COMPARISON

Apart from a whole spectrum of interesting speculations, which arise from the more complete findings in the above groups, it is possible to say that:

(1) On the basis of family structure and heterosexual development, the skyjacker group stands alone in presenting a consistent picture.

(2) In the vestibular area, they are closely related to several groups of law breakers. Strangely, although the frequency and intensity of dreams of paralysis and flight are identical with bank robbers, only skyjackers ever "flapped their wings" in interview, while relating the material.

Is it not strange that men, who seem to be clearly unbalanced and to feel that they are *above the law* during solitary "stands" against it, apparently have trouble *with the law of gravity,* as exhibited by neurotic involvement with flight, space, and movement?

In contrast, it is interesting that men, who feel and comport themselves, as if they were *under law,* who have "standing," are not unbalanced, nor do they have serious trouble with the *law of gravity.*

# XV

## The Man, Flight, and Society

The first thirteen chapters in this volume have concerned themselves with the individual offenders in this crime. One might say, how the man "stood" in relationship to himself and ultimately to the crime he committed. Certain consistencies, of rather surprising quality, appeared.

With the aid of controls, then, the question is raised, where do these men "stand" in comparison with other men? Here we come upon an interesting fact: In spite of the beauty of the degree of involvement these men have with flight and space, as seen in their dreams and waking interests, *this alone is not determinative.*

The characteristic of neurotic involvement with space seems to separate the law-abiding from certain groups of law breakers. From this, one might infer that one's sense of reality, if based upon a disturbed perception of the basic physical law (gravity), would, in moments of stress, be characterized by unstable concepts of the laws of man. Thus, one disturbed in such a fashion might act out *a* crime in which he saw himself as "standing against the forces." But which crime?

This study seems to suggest that the final determinant rests within the *family from which a man comes, and the symbols to which it originally reacted.* (Remember the differences between bank robbers and skyjackers.)

205

## THE EXPANDED FAMILY

Just as people respond to their original family, so too do we all tend to react to the larger family. This larger family includes the nation and its titular head, the President or "father of the country." Families have histories and certain events in their past influence their current attitudes and activities.

We have examined these men in connection with their individual functions and comparable functions in other groups of men. Now let us use a little time to view them in connection with their broader family—us.

This nation, when founded as a democracy, was seriously warned by some of its founders that a *democracy could become a mob*. It is not my purpose here to argue that we have become a mob, but it would certainly be no exaggeration to say that in recent years we've had a great deal of trouble *with* mobs.

The current tendency toward mobs is evident. The Congress spends months deliberating on economic and welfare matters to avoid just such mobs.

My basic statement relative to the findings in these men pre-supposes that the sense of the possible and of the impossible is rooted in our earliest experience with gravity. The study suggests that those with the *greatest* level of disturbance in this function perform our *craziest* crimes. However, we are all subject to disturbance in this area, and to *suggestion* from significant events which take place in connection with space.

As a case in point, for the moment let us develop a theory of the history of the particular crime committed by these men. This is the history of their *extended family,* the nation and the world, in connection with flight and theft.

## THE GROWTH OF AN IDEA

The fuel for man's motion and his actions lies in his capacity to "have an idea," and then to act upon it. To paraphrase Koheleth, there is really nothing new under the sun. Most ideas, unlike Athena, do not spring full-grown from the head of Zeus. They have their own histories and pass unheralded and unheeded from mind to mind and from generation to generation.

Apart from Greek and Roman mythology, about which most of us have at least a rudimentary knowledge, the most significant "event" involving the flight of man (among most Western Europeans) undoubtedly lies within the mythos of the Christian religion. During the ministry of Jesus, it is said that he was involved in at least three miracles in which gravity was defied. The first two, the walking on the water and the raising of Lazarus, are not of fundamental importance for our purposes. The third miracle, however, remains a major factor in the Christian religion. In fact, it may be its major assertion. That "He arose!" has been for centuries in the minds of many the major proof of his deity, and has pointed directly to both the existence and the nature of God.

The resurrection and ascension of Christ is an idea that today is communicated throughout the Western world to our youngest children, and many of them have been encouraged to believe that if their behavior has been appropriate, on the occasion of their demise they will join him *above* in that other, better place. Let us assume in the growth of the idea of man's flying that this image may well be *one facet* in the thinking of those individuals who have sought to defy the force of gravity. The id obviously yearns for such a possibility and Christianity and aviation (including the space effort) have stimulated it.

The Wright brothers, in 1903, demonstrated that man could *defy gravity* momentarily, with his own technological design. (A comic at the State Department asserts that "probably Wilbur skyjacked on Orville.") In the year 1927, Charles Lindberg contributed to the realization of the dream by adding a new ingredient, when he demonstrated that man could defy the power of gravity long enough to fly across a *body of water* between two continents. The infectious power of this innovation was so great, that 273 men elected to follow his example. In time, this urge to emulate the "Lone Eagle" became such a public nuisance that society was forced to institute controls in the form of laws prohibiting such acts. In 1936, one of these imitators was a man who came to be nicknamed "Wrong-way Corrigan." He added a new ingredient to the image, which was that a man could *defy gravity* between two continents, and simultaneously *defy the law*.

In 1941, Rudolf Hess further extended the syndrome, when he defied gravity and the law and became, simultaneously, *a traitor* to his father figure. Although this flight, by Hess, included the theft of an airplane, nevertheless, the pilot who departed in the plane was also the one who flew it and abandoned it. Hess was the first widely publicized hijacker.[1] His crossing of a hostile border was a new innovation, and became a widely practiced political tactic when the iron curtain settled in.


## THE EUROPEAN BEGINNING

Between the years 1945 and 1950, an outbreak of hijackings occurred in the red bloc countries. These hijackings were dominantly characterized by the crossing of hostile borders and all but one involved *groups of people*.[2] In most cases at least one of the group could pilot the plane if need be. These mobs constitute the earliest form of the phenomena.

In August of 1947, ten Rumanians landed in a forbidden Turkish area. One crewman had been killed because he refused to pilot the plane to Turkey.

In April of 1948, thirty Czechs seized a plane in mid-air and

[1] The first known incidence of armed intervention of aircraft came to light thirty years after the perpetration of the crime. In 1930, a Pan American pilot (Capt. Byron D. Richards) had his plane commandeered by rebels, in order to propagandize a revolution, and was forced to land at Arequipa, Peru. After being held for several days, the pilot and his crew were permitted to fly out, through the interventtion of British officials. This diversion was not reported (and hence, received not one whit of publicity at the time) until 1961, when the same pilot was skyjacked in the first year of American skyjackings. The story appeared in *The New York Times*, August 3, 1961.

[2] This group of hijacking crimes was not singled out as having particular characteristics, since there were so many movements, (by truck, digging under fences, etc.) to escape the Red Block countries, at the time.

forced it to land in the U.S. Zone. In May, 1948, another Czech plane was hijacked to Germany, when five non-Communist passengers forced the pilot, at gun point, to bring them into Germany. In the same year, two men used guns to force a Yugoslav pilot to land a commercial aircraft in Italy. The next hijacking was by twenty-three Rumanians to Austria in June of 1948. In that same month, a plane was forced to land in Turkey with twenty Bulgarians aboard.

In July of 1948, on a flight from Macao to Hong Kong, bandits diverted the plane for purposes of robbing the passengers.

In September of 1948, eight armed Greek passengers overpowered the crew of a commercial airliner, on an Athens-to-Salonika flight, and forced the pilot to land in Yugoslavia. The rebellious passengers were communists, and this was the first hijacking, in reverse, to an iron curtain country.

In April of 1949, a student aboard a Soviet Rumanian Airways plane held up the pilot with a revolver and forced him to fly to Greece. This is the only hijacking by an individual in this period. In December of that same year four Rumanians forced the pilot of a Soviet Rumanian airliner transport plane to fly to Yugoslavia. Again in December 1949, sixteen Poles hijacked a Polish Airliner to Denmark. The Poles, like all the others before them, were granted political asylum.

It must be here noted that we, the West, established the principle of political asylum in connection with aircraft theft. The iron curtain, which had developed after World War II, became increasingly rigid. It became the "in" thing for political refugees, amid great fanfare, to flee from one bloc to the other. The Berlin Blockade had been the clear sign of the mutual intransigence between the systems. It was followed by the events of the fifties, described below.

In the years 1958 and 1959, two major developments occurred. The first was the sudden freezing of railroad and highway travel isolating the city of Berlin from the Western world. The second was the beginning of Castro's revolution in Cuba. The first of these problems, "the second Berlin blockade," was solved by some

277,000 flights of multiengine aircraft, each of which, again pen-
etrated a *hostile barrier*. Each such flight constituted a significant
act of heroism by its crew.

Every act mentioned here: the Ascension, the flights of the
Wright brothers, of Lindberg, of Corrigan, of Hess, of the political
agents, and especially the flights of the Berlin Blockade, has attracted worldwide attention. In the case of the Berlin flights, these
made repeated headlines for eighteen months. (They always linked
individual bravery, flight, and hostile borders.)

## THE CUBAN START

In the same year as the beginning of the Berlin Blockade, the
first theft of an aircraft in the Cuban area occurred. Certain Castro
supporters diverted a Cuban commercial airliner in an attempt to
join Castro at another end of the island. That plane crashed and
all were killed. This event received little publicity other than in
Cuba, itself, but probably played a significant part in the infectious
events that followed. It represented something very close to an
imitation of our airlift over the Russians to Berlin. They planned
to fly in support to Castro, but failed.

In December of 1959, Castro's revolution succeeded; and in
January of 1960, John F. Kennedy became President of the United
States. Immediately on the heels of these two events, a sizeable
illegal flow of aircraft began to move *from* Cuba *to* the United
States. At this stage no real new ingredient had been added. A pilot
defied gravity across a hostile body of water, which represented,
in addition, a hostile political barrier. In their actions the pilots
acted as traitors to their own homeland, and were manifestly politi-
cally and economically motivated. This change is the first mutation.
One might think of this procedure as the "Miami Airlift" dedicated
to the proposition that Cuban pilots did not aspire to chop cane
for the fatherland. In spite of murder committed aboard several of
these craft, this time *we, the Americans again granted political asylum* and fixed the concept of immunity from law for the offenders.

(A year later we were ready to pass a death sentence for men who would treat *us* that way.)

## THE AMERICAN START

*In 1961, the newest and, up to then, most dangerous innovation entered the picture.* In that year, for the first time, the man who stole the airplane was *not himself a pilot,* but was a *passive rider* who achieved control of the flight by the use of a weapon.[3] That completely changed the nature of the game by at least ten thousand fold. Up to this point, such a theft had demanded an aviation competence sufficiently adequate to manage a multiengine plane. Only limited numbers could participate. Beyond this point, "anybody could play," provided he had a dollar and a half to buy a pocket knife, or fifty-nine cents to buy a can of insect repellent, or provided he was clever enough to look into the nearest garbage can for some strange object that he could call a bomb. Of course, he had to have enough cash to buy a one-way ticket on some airplane, or be clever enough to buy his ticket with a forged check, or be knowledgeable enough to charter a private airplane, in which latter event, he would not be expected to pay until the end of the flight.

Thus the idea gradually grew in the national press, from mob actions to single heroic acts by "Birdmen," into one in which even the most inept and unprepared could play. For the purpose of this record, pilots up through 1960 are described as *hijackers*; and the passive riders, beginning in America in 1961, are described as *skyjackers*. The true political offender, who began in Europe in the late forties, probably went under cover at this point.

For the moment I should like to consider the fact that these crimes (committed on American commercial airlines during this period) were originally more commonly a function of single individuals with a common profile than of a group. There are, nonethe-

---

[3] Although there had been scattered "singles" before, what we are concerned with here is repeated events. This is the second mutation.

less, even in these separate events, not only certain psychological parallels among skyjackers, but also between skyjacking and mob behavior. In those instances involving more than one skyjacker most of the parallels also hold true, so that the act of the individual seems to shade subtly into that of the group. One group of two (Gladys and George) has been described.

## MOBS

Skyjacking appears to be a function of our society and involves collective behavior.

Of all the forms of collective behavior, mob activity is the most goal-oriented and the most dependent upon leadership for its direction. Besides mobs, collective behavior theory is applied to: rumor, *fads* and fashions, *crazes,* mass hysteria, public opinion, and audiences. I would propose that skyjacking has been a mob and a craze, but may now be a fixture.

Mobs are generally bent upon an aggressive act such as lynching, looting, or the destruction of property. It is not usually randomly destructive, but tends to be focused on some one target or identity. The target of mob aggression is frequently an individual or group (but rarely another mob) that is resented or perceived as a source of frustration. The socially defined nature of mob action is evident in "scapegoating," in which aggression is *displaced* from the real sources of frustration, such as economic distress, to a group or individual defined as a legitimate object of hostility. Although a mob is defined as two or more people, I suggest that skyjackers are also part-of-a-mob that is spread out over both time and space. Mobs represent men whose collective personality is different from their usual individual characteristics. This process occurs through psychological mechanisms such as imitation, suggestion, and emotional contagion, through which dissemination takes place, and in the presence of anonymity and restricted attention, which neutralize ordinary behavior anchorages. Perhaps, for example, the emotional change that sweeps over a nation as it plunges into war, or rebels against it, is similar to this. We, as a nation, have been involved in the Vietnamese debacle and the Bay of Pigs disaster during the beginning of skyjacking. Moreover, there was a large-scale movement of men toward the Caribbean as a result of our response to the threat of the missile crisis. We have been an agitated people since 1960 and partly because of the influence of JFK's vigor.

To consider the possibility raised here, one must be willing to consider the public at large as constituting a mob. Even though the single skyjackers have no direct, personal contact with each other, because of the ubiquity of our news media and the overall uniformity of our population's understanding of certain symbols, we have a situation in which *it is as if* the men had contact with each other.

Perhaps the clearest manifestation of the immense communicability of the images surrounding skyjacking is to be seen in certain events of the year 1960. At that point, there had been only three skyjackings from Cuba to the United States over a period of perhaps ninety days. Then a passive armed rider appeared in Australia. In order for this event to occur in Australia, it was necessary for the "idea" to travel halfway around the globe, to cross the equator, to move from a Spanish culture to an Anglo-Saxon culture, and be translated from Spanish to English. In addition, it even had to change its political position, since at that time all of the flights were moving from a Red-dominated nation toward the Western world, whereas this one attempted to go from a democracy to a Communist state. Such an immediate and complicated communication can occur only in the case of an idea so basic as to be understood by any man, regardless of his race, intellect, social background, or academic achievement. Such images are *surely* basic. Gravity and the need to escape it are basic.

In regard to the factor of emulation, it is interestng how one skyjacker can discuss with great avidity and compassion the attempts of another. Prior to their own attempts, many of the men had studied other efforts with great care, and a clear identification is demonstrable among and between the cases so that they generally know the names of several other offenders.

## SYMBOLS

A symbol, if clearly delineated, is one which is interpreted in the unconscious of *all men*. The fact that *certain men* respond specifically, whereas others do not, is probably more a matter of coincidental side pressures upon them at that moment, or of the relative inadequacy of their defense systems (or specificity of their family patterns of behavior) that render them unable to ward off the "need to speak," than anything else. Most of the offenders had been involved in intense pressure for months prior to their attempts.

If an act by one man stands for him alone as a symbol for some highly unique aspect of himself, or if the act has common meaning but passes relatively unnoticed, there will be no replication. But *if* the act expresses feelings common to the group, and *if* the act is thoroughly publicized as puzzling to the authorities, and seems to gain public attention and to have achieved "success" for the performer, the appeal for replication can be extremely compelling. By the same token, the "language of the medium" generally will not be understood by those who have the legal control at the time and in the place of the act. The "ins" never seem to understand what the "outs" are complaining about. On the other hand, the "outs" who act in moments of great personal turmoil are often as puzzled as anyone else that *they* acted as they did. Quite often the offender has very strong feelings of disapproval of his own actions. One skyjacker saw the act as treason and felt that all traitors should go before a firing squad.

## REINFORCEMENT

Conditions of unanimity and intensity produce a "circular reaction," which is a type of interstimulation, wherein the response of one individual reproduces the stimulation in another. The press and television are important here. In normal conditions, there is merely "interpretative interaction," rather than undiluted stimulus behavior. This probably is involved in those moments in which both space activity and skyjacking get well under way with both on the newspaper front page the same day.

It may seem too much of a strain for the imagination of some to conceive of a group of skyjackers, separated by thousands of miles and even by several years, agreeing upon a norm. If, however, one keeps in mind that we, the non-skyjackers, are a part of this mob and that we serve as unknowing interconnecting links between them (including the symbol-building capacity of the press), it may be a little easier. (It would also help to view the matter with a time/sight lens from space. The perspective would change.) In this regard, it seems quite important to me that in as many attempts as there have been, most guns have not been fired. Blood has rarely flowed. (A mutation is now possible which could change all of this.) It is quite clear that the uniformity of procedure does not lie in the management of the aircrews, which is pretty irregular. It lies in a consistent, self-imposed "code of the road" that the men use themselves in spite of their anxiety and obvious illness.


## THE DISPARATE MOB

Perhaps what was intended in the original designation of group behavior was a more or less usable concept based upon early twentieth-century phenomena in which a mob was comprised of individuals operating in sight of one another and within ready hailing distance. This description could be employed to consider what takes place in a single plane among its occupants in a single skyjacking.

In the latter part of the twentieth century, it has become obvious that we must construct a new concept of mob activity in which the individuals are not in line of sight, not within hailing distance, and not acting in a discrete time period in relationship to the activities of the others within their mob. I would propose that the term "disparate mob" should be employed to characterize these phenomena. In such a concept, the reactive mass would of necessity be the entire population, tightly tied together by our nearly instant news media, which have the power to put us all almost in "line of sight and hailing distance of each other." Since one is dealing with a much larger population mass, the definition of "discrete units of time" must obviously be extended to allow for lag-time commensurate with the larger mass.


## SYMBOL COMMUNICATION

How else might one explain the phenomena in which at one point in history a Vietnamese monk converts himself into a flaming torch to dramatize a political cause, only to have that same action duplicated on the steps of a university in Czechoslovakia a few years later by a student on the occasion of the Russian occupation of that nation? When this latter act is shortly followed by a similar one on the terrace of the United Nations in New York City, the immediate "line of sight and hailing distance" of the news media playing its part in infectious communicability is demonstrated.

This is perhaps not the moment to deal with this factor, but it must be stated that such a symbolic action is not a rigid and fixed act. It can be used by more imaginative men in more highly technological societies with far greater impact upon the conscience of a nation than that of one lonely figure going down in flames on the steps of a building. Herein lies the chief justification of this study. As long as skyjacking continues to run along as a continuing part of the national myth, it remains an incipient source of a possible mutant from which real terror could lie in the skies for the unmindful traveler. It has been harmless, though relatively expensive to date, but a rich nation and rich airlines can afford this little itch. We could not tolerate a mutant or hybrid of this symbolic act combined with another and more destructive one.

It must be clearly evident from the case material presented in previous chapters that there is a peculiar paradox here. These men had taken leave of their own lifelong patterns, of the rules of the organized society within which they lived. In their thinking, they were highly illogical and desperate, i.e., without rational reason. Reality be damned! Something had to change and they gambled life and limb in the process.

## NEW BEHAVIORAL NORMS

I continue to feel that a good part of the drive that powered the exponential rise of skyjacking in 1968, in addition to the meaning of the space effort of that year, was the very unsettling effect of the election in which all sorts of "emergent" norms were being acted out, from the President down to the bottom of society. Sharp changes in economy, politics, mores, and function are considered by many people to be the justification for use of emergency behavior norms. In that year, as a nation, we were a jumpy bunch, burning cities, assassinating prominent men, and occupying campuses. Not a small number of people, now in this country, would sacrifice their citizenship in order to escape these changes if they knew any place else to go. (It should be noted that presidential election years immediately precede a skyjacking surge. Such years are very disturbing for paranoid people.) There was, in addition, a sense in that year that things were quite out of control, that the established authority was without knowledge or intent—Vietnam had come to dominate and control.

A few years ago this nation became quite aggressive internally as well as externally. The Black stood up and walked. The student took the campus. And the adolescent took drugs. At various places, precipitating factors, coming to the attention of potential leaders, led straight to their organizing for action to do their "thing." In every area of this nation the establishment has been under attack by millions of Americans, each eager to be a part of the events of change. Some have been more desperate for acclaim and change than others. Some have been realistic in their efforts and others completely psychotic.

Our current tendency to individual heroics makes social control much more difficult, so that we have come to be one huge reactive mass. In the midst of it, self-appointed leaders arise, set goals for the reactive mass about them, and demonstrations begin.

The early response of the central government toward this instability was to assume it to be a natural consequence of the changes about to take place and they protected the leaders of change. The Supreme Court re-interpreted the law and the legislatures concurred. In many instances industry followed suit, sometimes knowingly and often unknowingly. Only a few old die-hards raised the alarm, "Too much change too fast?"

So, then, for some years we have been a reactive mass and most of us, in our fear of being "square" or "out of it," have wished some little corner of it all would touch upon our own dull lives. (Someone once described a friend of mind as being "an accident looking for some place to happen.") Many of us today are "mobs looking for some place to happen."

From the "top," the word has been "lots is going to happen— and don't you try to stop it." This idea has permeated our society, and I suspect it has played a strong part in the permissive attitude of both industry and government. Certainly it has been the norm aboard aircraft, for the skyjacker has known that if he must "do his thing," the roles have been assigned and the show may proceed. The common phrase is, "He's got his thing—let him do it!"

Let me emphasize this to be only *one* factor involved in what has transpired. I am only trying to point out that we have experienced a change in behavioral norm in which individual, self-appointed mob leadership is permitted and encouraged. These self-appointed leaders find themselves in conducive, strained situations that can be instantly crystallized, precipitated, and mobilized into almost magically rapid action.

In the face of it all, social controls have failed and it has become common for most people, who have been given the chance, to stand by passively and innocently while others "do their thing."

Periodically, certain specific individuals representing disguised but traditional values have stolen aircraft and because of our general permissiveness, they have had a modicum of success. Once the rules of a game are established, it may be hard to change, but the change may be taking place quietly in response to some of the current "backlash." The election of Richard Nixon is a moderate expression of change. His court is changing. The legislatures are tightening up. And it is reasonable to anticipate that industry will do the same. These changes in turn are bound to modify the attitudes of the public in the macrocosm as well as in the microcosm of a single aircraft.

If, then, the public at large has been a potential mob looking for a place to "happen" or "watch it happen," as a consequence of freed pressures and modified norms, then those little packets of people that comprise a *grouping* of passengers and crew are involved in situations characterized by *nearness* of people within which *roles and status* may be assigned. During flight, *attention is focused* upon an individual and upon an occurring situation that has the appearance of *spontaneity*. That is the description of mob activity.

## PASSENGERS

Why should it be that passengers have traditionally been passive? There is the realistic fear we all have of arguing with a gun, to be sure, but one senses something more than this. Several victims of skyjacking have submitted to detailed interviews from which I found that other factors were also important. Chief among them were the feelings: (1) "My God, history [notoriety] is being made, and I'm part of it. (2) Gosh, I wonder what I'll see in Cuba. (3) If they put us in a hotel, will there be any women? (4) That guy's really got guts, but me, hell, anybody can push me around. (5) Boy, will this ever get the bureaucrats off their asses for a while! (6) I'll bet that damned pilot feels funny as all get-out taking orders like that—I mean—well, he was the boss until a minute ago and now all of a sudden he's nothing."

So, here is exhibitionism and increased identity, curiosity, sexual longing, admiration and the wish to identify, hostility toward authority, and delight in iconoclasm. Simply by not doing anything to stop the action, the passengers had all of these additional delightfully enjoyable sensations for the price of their tickets.

Singularly important among the passenger reactions is the sense of hostility toward the government (which robs them of taxes) and birdmen (who rob them of their sense of pride). The wish of most is to be a part of showing *them* up. These attitudes are only slightly different (and only because of better defenses) from those of the skyjackers. To a greater or lesser extent, we are all earthbound and resentful of that fact.

The "scapegoating" of the plane (flag, nation, bureaucrats), the pilot (birdmen in general and astronauts in particular), and the "raping" of the hostess (little sisters, mothers, and the last woman who turned us down) is not just the activity of the skyjacker. He speaks for the mob, i.e., all of us, in his sick moment. Since the public knows the rules of the game as well as the major players, they sit quietly by for a free ride to Cuba. They know that the game, correctly played, makes them celebrities, too, among their circle of friends when they relate the tale. For a moment, too, they also run away from wives, mortgages, the Internal Revenue Service, and the church appeal.

## THE INDUSTRY AND PILOTS

The airlines would like to claim the lion's share of the acclaim for damage control, but this seems quite out of the question. The aircrew behavior is quite inconsistent, but the results are the same regardless of crew behavior. In regard to crews' being human and capable of responses to psychotic enthusiasm, one must not overlook the rather impressive individual who first convinced his wife and Army reserve superior that he had been designated to assassinate Castro and won their support, and who later enlisted the sympathies and assistance of the aircrew enough that he could let them hold his gun while he had a drink and return it to him after he finished.

Crews are just people and in crises they act like people, so there is no need for the airlines to amplify further the superman, superwoman myth by proclaiming that they have controlled the situation. An additional argument that might be added here in this regard is that *no crew has yet dissuaded either an armed black or an armed Cuban from his efforts.* If their technique and preparation is what we have been led to believe it is, some of these groups should have also yielded to the method. They have not.

*Can you imagine a plane crash in which neither the industry, the government, nor pilot's union insisted on a meticulous examination of every physical factor?* They understand the physical, and behave rationally toward it.

Actually, any simplistic explanation is doomed. There are many factors operating, and each is important at various levels of the event. Any individual addicted to "one-to-one cause and effect thinking" can hit a snag on every page of this volume. Times change, people change, circumstances change, physiology alters, politics rumble, war threatens, etc., and out of the aggregate of these forces emerge skyjackers with a variable rate of incidence.

From interview material of those most disturbed by neurotic involvement with space (skyjackers *and* bank robbers) it is quite clear that their *individual* acts in the commission of their crime were related to specific events in the space program, as well as to their basic instability, family constellation, and immediate situation of failure.

What is the overall possibility that we are all reacting, at some level, to the deep symbolic fact that reality, for us too, has changed? The impossible is no longer impossible. That which goes up does not *have to* come down according to the space program.

Is it possible that the success of our space effort might be related to our overall rising crime rate and political instability?

Knowing that the individuals here studied have a connection with the space effort, it was felt wise to study the whole skyjacker sample [4] from this point of view. This study appears in the next chapter. So far we have not gathered the same data on bank robbery incidence, but plan to do so.

[4] See Appendix B for a listing of all skyjacking to date.

# XVI
## Skyjacking and the Space Program

Some months ago a press release made an attempt to destroy the skyjacker image, through distribution of the true image of these men at a grass-roots level. The reporter did quite well in capturing the essence of the problem, even though he needed over half a page to cover the story. The Associated Press wire story threw out every factor, except that of the possible association with the space effort.

I shall not make an extended effort here to elaborate upon, or to prove, my contention. *The impression of a possible connection arises from the clinical material itself, with a clarity of such an order that one can flatly state, at least as far as these individuals are concerned, that their behavior had, as one of its determinants, a specific stimulus and excitement from this source.* These cases constitute a respectable fraction of the total.

One must remember that we are viewing mob function, with a circular restimulation, involving characteristic time lags and a multiplicity of factors. A simplistic mathematical approach that treats each space venture equally, without regard for the magnitude of the *element of novelty* involved in the technological advances, and that ignores the *basic national emotional climate* of the moment, and overlooks the tendency of fads and crazes toward entropy and mutation, is doomed.

On one occasion, after having shown my information to the medical director of the FAA, I was *told* that they had submitted it to their computer people, who had subsequently stated that "there was *no* correlation." It is true that an attempt at correlation, based on simplistic notions, will present a mildly unsatisfactory correlation, since a computer is incapable of being any smarter than the man who runs it. It is patently impossible to have *no* correlation, even if the machine is fed improperly. A suggestively satisfactory level of correlation results from proper feeding and subsequent intelligent inquiry.

Mathematics is not my thing, and it is not my intention here to venture upon the hallowed ground of statisticians, but I will briefly sketch certain concepts and data that provide a basis upon which one may assume mob function.

## METHOD

A reading team, whose function was to read *Time* magazine, over the period of the past twelve years, was created. They were to read it issue by issue and to score it according to a list of some forty factors, in terms of the major emotional concerns and interests of the nation.

Requests were sent to each of the three major television networks, to ask if they could state the amount of live television coverage, given at specific periods to the American space effort. In spite of the effort involved, all three networks kindly met our request.

Other individuals were hired to "spot-sample" three national newspapers, on a random basis, to determine whether there was a significant relationship between daily news and that which appeared in *Time* magazine. In addition, the "spot-sample" was intended to give us information, upon which to base the time lag for a weekly news magazine.

Mathematicians were engaged to begin a systematic plotting of the relationship between the space flights and the skyjackings.

## FINDINGS

In the beginning, these efforts were most unrewarding. The scale we were employing to visualize the events was too diminutive. It was only much later that we learned that the events had to be "blown up" to such a scale that a single day, of a single week, of a single year could be identified at a glance, in order that the periodic pulses, in relative relationship between the events, could become evident. But this was all months later. At first, we moved with little confidence in this area. Although the clinical material clearly indicated that the emotional input of the space programs was highly disturbing, our initial studies did not show that it had much impact.

A great deal of time was required to assemble all the data. Particularly difficult were data on skyjacking itself. Finally, the Department of State unearthed a study, by Turner,[1] which represented an exhaustive research of news sources on the subject. State gave the material to the FAA, and they computerized it. Since that time, it has been easy to keep up information on incidence. It is not known if Turner has been recognized for his contribution.

Reference is made, in Chapter III, to the years 1961, 1965, and 1968–69, which showed a relationship between major outbreaks of skyjacking and maturation of the Friendship, Gemini, and Apollo families of space vessels.

In time, various tools of ours suggested that *a political unrest factor was already present* in the society, at the time of these unusual space events. This was related to the fact that the space programs had been geared to presidential elections, in such a way that new families (and thereby risk) *followed* elections. Because of the stimulative effect of political years upon paranoid individuals, this came to be a part of our calculations.

We found that there has been a great range of intensity of news and television coverage of the space events. In the original series, in 1961, television had not yet recognized the salability of news on the subject, and very little time was given to the event. The space vessels were only up seconds, or minutes, at that time. Even so, as noted in Chapter III, the onset of both phenomena was closely clustered.

[1] James Turner, S.G., Lt. Col. U.S. Marine Corps, "Piracy in the Air," Naval War College, Newport, R.I., April 14, 1969 (RESTRICTED).

Our final conclusion is that, in 1961, a highly sensitive public (i.e., emotionally unexperienced) was suddenly struck by a very powerful stimulus and reacted sharply, with a cluster of skyjackings *here,* followed by an echo later in the year, from other nations, in the form of three skyjackings, including one in Russia.

In 1962, a less sensitive (i.e., more emotionally prepared) public responded again to the stimulus, but not nearly as quickly or as vigorously, in spite of greater news and television coverage. Fads tend to die down.

The year 1963 had little space activity (one space shot) and a slow, limited skyjacker response. There was nothing new during this period and the activity went almost unnoticed.

The year 1964 was a complete bust. Only one space shot (and that one by the Russians, who had the temerity to *fly a woman*). They promptly had a skyjacking. We had one, earlier in the year, following a great deal of news on what would occur the following year, related to dramatic engine tests and the like.

In 1965, both the press and television went wild with coverage of the new Gemini series. (They went so wild, in fact, that the public objected, in Congress, to the pre-emption of so much prime time for the coverage.) Apparently, the media had learned of the salability of the factor, and slightly overshot public acceptance.

The skyjacker did not respond quickly, because, by now, we were rather well conditioned about the matter. Various new factors came to be added along the way, such as live television (black and white at first, and later colored), space walks, space link-ups, and, finally, moon walks. It would greatly overextend this volume to attempt to relate these events, but we came, with time, to find them related to increases of skyjacking. After resisting the allure, through the first two space shots, we finally responded to the third, with a rash of skyjackings at a peak of news coverage and new innovations.

The year 1966 represented five American space shots over the year, each of declining importance and coverage. The rate of skyjacking reflected these factors.

The year 1967 had no space shots, although press coverage

remained fairly high. *In spite of this fact, skyjacking continued.* Unlike the year 1964, which almost completely died down, this year continued to sputter along. The response was often foreign, like the previously noted tendency for an "echo reaction" to what takes place here. This fact suggests, though, that the behavior has come to be built into our society, such that it could continue at some level, even if we abandoned space efforts tomorrow.

The year 1968 started with a bang, with great coverage of new boosters *which, for the first time, would put us ahead of the Russians, in the space race.* These were unmanned shots, but with live coverage. There were also a number of "Space Specials," anticipating what was to come later in the year. (President Johnson also accelerated the program, to get Apollo VIII into his administration, thereby bringing both a new space family and a presidential election year into exact temporal relationship.)

The effect of these combined relationships was dramatic. That early burst of national enthusiasm and pride fired off a proportionate skyjacking response. The news and skyjacking declined at the same rates. After three months of inactivity, the increased coverage by news specials, etc., began, and was accompanied by a proportionate response in skyjacking, over a three-month period.

On the heels of this period came Apollo VII, with the sustained flight of men, just before the attempt to orbit the moon. Coverage sharply increased, as did skyjacking, such that, beginning at this point, through Apollo XI, an almost exact pulsile movement began, in connection with each space shot, its news coverage, and its skyjacking incidence.

Through this period, if one allows for only the slightest consequence of purely random effect, one is obliged to consider at least one possibility. There is a direct correlation between an anticipated space shot and the suppression of skyjacking, i.e.: as news coverage, antecedent to the event, rises, skyjacking almost ceases. The period during which men are in space also has almost no skyjacking. The usual duration of these two factors, when combined, is about a month.

When, however, the shot is completed by the return of the astronauts to earth, and television coverage abruptly stops, skyjacking begins in earnest, within hours. This period lasts for about six weeks, with certain characteristic densities and pulses directly related to such accessory new inputs as trips abroad by the returning space heroes.

If one forgets the declining effect of a fad, and accumulating public resistance, it seems a little odd that Apollo VIII (first man orbit) has a slightly more specific American response than Apollo XI (first moon walk). However, it is interesting to note that Apollo XI, with the first live satellite television coverage to Europe (which created the world's largest television audience), caught a relatively unguarded foreign population off-guard and got a proportionate response from those areas through skyjacking.

A loss of specificity of cause and effect response, due to accumulating public resistance, had been anticipated to begin with Apollo XI, and was noted as a softening of U. S. response, although the world total held up by virtue of expanded TV coverage. At this point the prediction was made that its overall decline will continue, and that specific response to space activity will largely disappear, until the next tremendous increase in technical development, news coverage, and national response. There are thousands of suggestive details in this material, but as stated earlier, it's not my thing.

## Summation

These findings have been sufficient to suggest to me that the clinical connection, between the men who were examined and space activity, is possibly also true of the whole phenomenon. It clearly appears to be true of the beginnings and the most exciting periods and will decline now, as previously stated.

This finding would support the thesis that, regardless of the political rationalizations espoused by the men who have not been examined, they are probably moved by the same deep unconscious factors as that part of the sample we could examine.

# XVII

## In Conclusion

### ABOUT OURSELVES

We have nobody to blame for this mess but ourselves. That is you, and that is me. Our own agents made this thing possible in the beginning, by condoning it, by granting political asylum. The original offenders in this regard were Europeans. (See Appendix B, the early offenders in this regard.) It will be observed that the early flow was from Communist bloc nations to the West and that in the U.S. zone of Germany we (America) were quite active in granting political asylum. In particular, in the period 1959–1960, we repeated this error in connection with skyjackers who fled *from* Cuba to Miami. The original errors (precedent) were probably made by army men who were much influenced by the whole phenomenon of men breaking through the iron curtain.

They undoubtedly could not foresee the possibilities in the situation or have any knowledge of the history of piracy. Miami only followed precedent. Such an action (following a precedent) required no original thought; and in addition, we, as a nation, were deriving much glory from the fact that the citizens under "that upstart Castro" wanted to come to our lovely selves so badly that they would even kill to do it.

When the shoe was on the other foot, the following year, however, and we were humiliated to find that love of our lovely-selves would not hold our whole population here, and some of them were flying *to* that upstart, we fell into a panic.

Panic, unfortunately, is man's response to the unknown. We had not the slightest knowledge of what was involved, yet we undoubtedly demanded of Congress that it act *right now* to handle the circumstance.

Congress, with no knowledge of its own, could only fall back on the traditional tool of man's most fearful threat: the death penalty. There was no way for Congress to reflect anything other than our own panic and ignorance.

This set up two problems. The first problem is that the proposed penalty, although unacceptable to sane men, is one which seriously increases the likelihood that unbalanced men would be excited by it. At the same time, it put the issue squarely on the back of the Attorney General and the Justice Department. *We obliged them to stop the thing right now, even though we had given them the wrong tools to work with.* This has obliged them to adopt that whole series of attitudes which (earlier in this volume) brought forth my satire and spleen.

They have had no alternative, other than to fight in rural federal courtrooms. We obliged them to try to create, in those rooms, a substitute for understanding and control. These juries were faced with the fact that, if they did not act as good citizens, we would lose face and be in a bigger mess than ever.

I can't be critical of this chain of events. It never seriously occurred to me, as a psychiatrist, that these men should be examined psychiatrically. To make the matter even more embarrassing, in the volume *Some Skunks and Other Cases,* I had been elaborating theoretical considerations directly bearing on the matter for years. This concept did not occur to me until the interview with two offenders "back to back," *and it would not have occurred to me if I had seen them on separate days.* It probably did not occur to other psychiatrists for this same reason.

An attempt has been made here for each of you to make this same discovery, through the case material offered. The real impact of interview cannot be brought to you, with the color, sounds, odors, pauses, and the rest of it, but I believe enough comes through.

Perhaps, after seeing this material, you and I and our representatives in Congress, can begin a more logical course.

I firmly believe that an informed democracy is capable of resolving its problems, even when a little embarrassment is involved.

## ABOUT THE OFFENDERS

Essentially, the skyjacker appeared to be driven to commit his extraordinary crime by a combination of an intense sense of *unreality* and clear *suicidal intent*. Substantial evidence has been accumulated to the effect that the skyjacker developed an inordinate awareness of his personal inability to maintain a stable physical equilibrium, vertically as well as both on a lateral and on an angular axis. His psychic disequilibrium appears to have clear associative patterns with his physical disequilibrium. The problems in the psychic area probably began in the vertical axis (affective processes), and subsequently implicated first the lateral and then the angular axes (thinking process). Symptoms were often expressed in terms of movement and symbolic chains of action.

Equilibratory defects create great difficulties in achieving psychic homeostasis interpersonally and intrapersonally. Men must cope with external reality and those who fail to attain homeostasis build up futile rage over their inability to do so. The result is the compensatory development of a delusion of their omnipotent capacity to rise above that restriction, which is expressed both when they are awake and when they are asleep. The crime of skyjacking is uniquely suited to accommodate the acting-out of that delusion and to vent intrapersonal and interpersonal pressures all at once.

Inasmuch as one has to be capable of grasping reality, in order to respond to the threat of punishment, to the skyjacker the threat of punishment can only be totally meaningless or else constitute an additional trigger effect toward activating his suicidal intent. Clearly, it is not merely futile, but foolhardy, to rely on any form of punishment in any rational plan designed to have a constructive effect on the problem of skyjacking as a whole.

## ABOUT CONTROL

For effective control of skyjacking, we must look elsewhere, and the following steps may well be worthy of practical application.

1. Negotiations toward establishing international agreement that

would acknowledge the *medical nature* of the problem. Such agreement would insure the *immediate return of all offenders* for hospitalization, study and disposition. I believe that sufficiently publicized international agreement on automatic repatriation would put a stop to the crime in short order.

2. Broad dissemination of the findings of medical research, such as those presented in this volume. For example, stressing the involvement of sexual inadequacy in the crime, together with its repressed incestuous content, would have a dissuasive effect on potential skyjackers.

3. Addition of women to the aerospace program would diminish the notion that "flight" is a male prerogative.

4. *The elimination of the death penalty and the certainty of protracted incarceration* would deflate the notion that one was "gambling with fate." The number of attempts eliminated by such a measure would be quite large. It would also facilitate negotiations with other nations that do not apply such penalties.

5. The findings of this study suggest the need for further research, to be conducted, ideally, in a research facility independent of, but cooperating with, existing agencies, thereby providing for the free interchange of data and ideas.

### Afterthought

In writing these conclusions, I was propped up on the bed with my youngest daughter, Marianna, age three months, cradled in my arm. At that moment, my youngest son, Pat, age three, bounded into the room and bounced on the bed, with great vigor. Marianna gave a tremendous start, with uncontrolled spastic muscle contraction, and *changed her mood completely,* as reflected by loud cries and agitated movement.

My thought at the moment was, "So what; he just jiggled her ear a little, and we take that sort of thing for granted." Right?

# Appendix A

## CRYPTO-VESTIBULAR DATA

Aside from the familial, psychic, interpersonal, and acute situational factors that seemed to set these men apart from the rest of the population, there is a sensory factor of real importance, which is possibly physio-physical. The sensory organs of vision, smell, hearing, tactility, and touch might be viewed as "superficial" when compared with the vestibulum. The eye "sees" rather directly with an immediate imagery related to the perceived object. The other senses function similarly. The vestibulum, however, speaks two languages, the first of which we know about in connection with bodily movements of such gross proportion as to be inescapable even at a conscious level of recognition. This first language, like that of the eye and the other "superficial" senses, is an "almost" instantaneous one and is "read" directly. The second language of the vestibulum (the crypto-vestibular speech)[1] is subliminal in intensity, chronic in character, and almost entirely sensed through other organs (i.e., the eye, muscle tone, vagal distribution, and endocrine responses). It originates in motion, but also through the stimulation of the vestibulum via the efferent limb, as a consequence of cerebral interrogation. Thus, this language might be con-

[1] It must be clear that I see the superego as being evolved from gravity and gravitational inertial awareness. Two authors have assumed in their writings that the vestibulum is the forerunner of the superego. A. Peto, Unpublished Manuscript, "A Vestibular Forerunner of the Superego " (New York); O. Isakower, "On the Exceptional Position of the Auditory Sphere," *International Journal of Psychoanalysis* (1939), vol. 20, pp. 340—348.

sidered to be silent or cryptic. In the speech forms in common use, we apparently lack terms that refer directly to the perception of this sense. We speak of sensations received in this way by compared action or by analogy to the sensation of another organ, but more commonly in terms of variant body image. It cannot be otherwise—the afferent impulse has been diffused into multiple other organs via the vagus chiefly and is "read" accordingly.

This language is far more commonly used than we ordinarily recognize. For example, two people, both seated, are engaged in a discussion of their relationship and of personal events. One says, *"I'm lower than a snake's belly.* I was really *set up* for a good party, but I was *knocked flat* when I saw her there." The friend replies, "You must have really *fallen* for her act." The first replies, "I *stood* it as long as I could, but when she acted like I was supposed to *crawl,* I just *blew up.* A fellow has to *stand up* for his rights sooner or later." The friend to whom he was complaining says, "But wait, you've got me kind of *mixed up.* You tell me she was trying to *look down* on you, but I thought you kind of had her *up on a pedestal."* "Oh no," comes the reply, "She's just real *low down.* But I don't know why I'm trying to talk to you about this anyway. You're *higher than a kite* today and would just *turn it all around."*

Now examine the foregoing conversation in which the body images of two seated speakers (and of a third party who is absent) revolve in space, rise, fall, and angulate in all directions. If one were to understand this conversation literally, all three parties would be acrobats and would daily risk their lives in the described activities. If one or another of them were not killed in the acrobatics, they would at least be physically exhausted and experience immense amounts of vestibular and proprioceptor inputs as a result of the activity. Herein lies the secret of the crypto-vestibular language. From the commonality of all inner ears, and the commonality of sensation, both pleasurable and unpleasurable, that we all experience in these different forms of acrobatic activity, there comes an experiential oneness for us all. In this language, to stand erect with the feet firmly planted upon the ground is the basic "given." Any variation from this "given" posture, as read chiefly by the movement of the head, has a physical, symbolic, and emotional commonality of content. We cannot describe the sensations themselves, but we can describe the movement that would produce them. It is this crypto-vestibular language that we use with such frequency and with such intimacy of content that we are unaware of its usage.

Some of the material in this chapter is clearly vestibular, some very possibly, while some requires imaginative interpretation to be so labeled, but I believe such an effort to be justifiable. The recurrent nature of some of these responses, even though *diametrically opposite* to each other, is exciting. Their exact reversal is more a cause for close scrutiny than for exclusion.[2]

Let me suggest that the reader simply lean back at this point and allow himself to *feel* the material drawn from the first thirteen cases as it endlessly repeats its distant but regular themes.

## BRIAN

DREAMS—"Early dreams? Well, I had one in which I was always *paralyzed.* It felt as if *my body weighed a ton.* My body was *heavy, heavy, heavy,* and *I couldn't move it.* The nights were horribly unpleasant because it always seemed something *awful* was about to happen." These dreams were a part of his definition of "something awful," but in addition there was a vague general apprehension. The dreams themselves and the unpleasant sense upon retiring *"continued as late as nineteen* or twenty years of age, and, *maybe, even last year."*

SPORTS—"I wasn't much good in sports, *probably it was my coordination.* Generally I was chosen last for teams. I often played at home with my sisters."

MOVEMENT—"I was very *fond of driving,* once I started, although it was *a little late.* To be able to get into a car and drive long distances seemed to have the ability to *clear my head,* particularly if

---

[2] In Bender's work, although marked retardation generally accompanied her sample, there were instances of seemingly paradoxical acceleration or precocity.

I was really *down* or someone had made me feel particularly little. Flying—it was *pure exultation to break free of the ground,* to be so *high above* the cold earth and the *little people* upon it. When my headaches were unbearable, I would fly away from home every other week and the minute *we took off the headaches would stop.* They would resume on landing when I returned home. The most attractive suicidal thought I had involved *jumping from a twentieth-story window,* or some other *high place."*

BODY SENSATIONS—"Quite often my *body feels extremely heavy,* even when I am awake, particularly if I feel *depressed.* At such times, too, my *head seems light or giddy.* Even mild nerve *medicines tend to make me quite dizzy* and it is very difficult for me to take them. *I didn't drink for the same reason."*

## ELMER

EARLIEST MEMORIES—"The earliest thing I can remember in life was of being used by my older sister as a doll. She *made me stay* in her buggy and *wouldn't let me get up.* If I tried to *get up* I was *spanked.* It used to make me as mad as anything, but *I couldn't fight back."*

DREAMS—"I was afraid a monster would get me. *I was all slow motion.* My hands and feet were *made of lead.* In sports it was a lot the same thing. I was awful *clumsy.* I used to dream pretty often about being *paralyzed.* There would be something after me, but *I couldn't move.* My arms and legs *just wouldn't move.* Those were terrible dreams and *even now, I occasionally have them."*

SPORTS—"I was *not good at sports* and tried to *avoid them* any way I could. I had a lot rather *go off in the woods* by myself. I spent an awful lot of time *walking.* It seemed to *make me feel better."*

MOVEMENT—"As I told you, when I was younger, *I used to walk a lot* when I was upset, and later, as soon as I could buy a car, *I drove and drove.* It seemed to calm me an awful lot. As a child I got *car sick. My body often feels heavy.* When I was in Washington at the Russian Embassy, it seemed to *weigh a ton.* It was *lighter going up* the steps when I thought I could go to Russia than it was when I *came down* the steps after I found out I couldn't go. *I don't drink,* not just because I don't think it's right, but it makes me very, *very dizzy* in a hurry and things get all *mixed up.* I thought that *draggy feeling* was a part of my cancer."

## BOB

DREAMS—"Oh, repeated dreams when I was a kid? I was always *paralyzed.* Something would be after me and I just couldn't move; my body *wouldn't respond* and I would wake up in a terror. Yes, *I still dream* that once in a while."

SPORTS—"Mostly I was inactive in sports except for *long-distance running.* It seemed like when I would *run for a long time* it tended to *clear my head,* I would feel *exultant* after a *good run.* Mostly I had hobbies, I collected hundreds of things. If I hadn't of been very neat, there wouldn't have been room to keep them. It seemed like giving up anything gave me a great feeling of sacrifice and a sharp sense of *loss.* I had hundreds of pen ball points and I held them in a box with a *magnet."*

MOVEMENT—"Just before I hijacked the plane, I was really *depressed* and at times I felt like I was a *sleepwalker.* At times like that if I would *walk a lot,* it seemed to *help calm me down* and made my *body feel better.* It was lighter. I was just awfully *tired,* I could *hardly move my body,* and I thought it was because I was *losing* at least one or two hours of *sleep* every night studying. As a child I was often *car sick."*

## DICK

EARLIEST MEMORY—"Earliest memory is of waking up *on a blanket on the floor,* the light was very dim, and I *couldn't rise to sit up.* It was *before I could walk.* It seems fantastic to me sometimes, but I have some very dim memories like this."

DREAMS—"Sometimes I've dreamed I've been naked at school, and sometimes I dreamed I was *running from a monster.* I was *paralyzed* and *couldn't escape.* I sort of *froze up* and *couldn't get away.* It's come back several times. More often I've had dreams of my bed being full of scorpions. *I've been on my feet,* it was like having the *D.T.s.* It was like a sea or swarm of scorpions on the floor, *I don't know if it was a dream or a hallucination.* The *dreams of the monster went through my teens* and the one of the *scorpions* 10-11-15-16-19 plus the twenties."

SPORTS—"I felt I was *bullied around* on the playground. I *couldn't speak very well* and at seven or eight I had to *learn to talk* all over because *my speech was thick.* It was like I had a Southern drawl."

MOTION—*"I can't drive very well, I don't judge distance.* As a student pilot, at sixteen, I had twelve hours and forty-five minutes dual before I soloed. I *learned slowly,* my *attention would wander.* Sometimes I'd gaze out of the airplane, *staring at the ground,* and I couldn't hear the instructor because of the engine roar, and I forgot some of my classroom instructions, too. I had *very little proficiency,* just barely enough to solo. The *airplane never did feel like a part of me.* When I'd turn the plane, *I'd lean away from the bank.* I wasn't really afraid of it, but *I'd lose a little altitude* on turns, and my timing and *control coordination was off.* Well, I was worn out. I was *physically tired,* I was *dense, my speech was incoherent most of the time.* I like model airplanes. I hardly ever indulged in any *sport* like baseball or basketball, I like to *swim* some. I never got in any school sports."

BODY SENSATIONS—"Everywhere I've gone, somebody has *gotten me under some sort of drug,* and I can *barely remember* what's going on. The fact is they're playing with my brain golgi cells. In the Army reserve I was *weak and thick and slow.* They thought I was *lazy* too. They were shouting at me. Unless I could sleep late of a morning, I was very *dense and stupid* and *went around raving.* I was *incoherent.* At night I *can't turn my mind off.* I'd just as soon be awake as asleep because I have *nightmares.* When I go to sleep, *I'm not aware of it,* I just *pass out,* time stops. When I wake up in the morning, there is *no apparent time* interval. Somebody, I feel, has been *reaching me* for five years. This isn't hallucinations, it must be *auditory*. There's a *time capsule* dissolving in my head."

# MARK

EARLIEST MEMORIES—"I recall a *red rocker, little cars,* I imagine at about five years old. I remember *weekend bus rides.* We used to go on *hikes.*"

DREAMS—"Really sometimes *I can't tell my dreams at night from things I feel in the daytime.* One thing I'm sure was a dream I often had was I was *drowning.* It was really bad. I was *going down, down, down, trying to get up* and saying, *'Why did I jump* in the water?' And there were often *things that were after me and I couldn't get away.*"

SPORTS—"I was *afraid to play ball* in front of the other guys. I don't know, when Mr. C——— asked me to play, why I turned him down, I don't know. I did, though. Usually I *played at home* in the back yard *with my sisters.*"

MOTION—"I *didn't learn to drive early,* we didn't have a car. I'd a lot *rather work on the engine* and things like that than actually drive one. When I learned to fly, I soloed in about eight hours. *Oooh, that was the best thing!* It was a *strange feeling* the first time *I went up,* it was scary. I don't know whether you would call it *sensation or fright,* but it was in between. It was hard to say, I knew I wanted to fly the airplane and I guess you could say it was an exciting sensation, something you weren't afraid of, but yet, you don't really have any fear, really. *I don't think I was too sharp on turns.* I tried to be right on the money, but you know, we actually did two or three of them, that was all, *we didn't go into it. On turns,* I'd pull away from it, like *you're looking out the window, you start to bank, right away you start to fall so you pull the other way.* I think it's a natural reaction. *I never owned a car.* One time *in a spin, my face swole out,* just felt like my *mouth was being pulled open,* and I knew I couldn't be pulling that many G's. I wasn't going that fast. *I didn't dance,* I didn't care for it. Just before my trouble, when I got *upset,* I got a moonlight job as a *chauffeur,* anything for peace and quiet. I'd been living around there all my life, places I'd know blindfolded, *I couldn't find my way in and I couldn't find my way out.* I thought, *'What's going on here?'* I had a trip to X Street, right up close to Y, in fact I used to play near a small pit and it's a tricky place to get at, but I could walk into it blindfolded. When I'm driving, I drive out, and heck, I get up to the place, and *I can't find my way out, just tied.* My wife, maybe everything will be okay, I try again, try talking to her *walking out* before you . . . like sometimes I'd go to work, I'd get on the bus, and *find myself somewhere I shouldn't be. I don't know how to explain the feeling I got. I got to go,* nothing can stop me, nothing. *It's something I've never experienced before and I tried acting, walking around the house. I didn't know what's wrong, I wasn't myself* it seemed like. *What's wrong with me,* I never could *understand* what she meant. I can't say, it just seemed *I didn't want to be around anybody or afraid* to be around the people. I'd get a sensation like—I don't know what you might call it, *gotta keep moving.* A *tall, tall man* and he kept saying you have to get off, you have to *get off,* and I didn't want to *get off.* I didn't want to *sit down* and I didn't want to *get up.* Then I remember screaming, I *feared* for my life, *'Can I stay here, can I stay here?'* Then all this business like *I'm falling,* somebody was *pulling* on me or *pulled* me back, I don't know what. And then I was *walking, walking,* trying to say, *'I'm here, here, I want to go home.'* I don't know how to explain it. *I never had a feeling like that before.* It seemed like *everything was kind of going around.* In the jail I had to *find my way back* into the doors, and I *couldn't find the doors.* I've always *liked to walk,* I don't know whether that's wrong or not, I don't know, all my life I've always *liked to walk.* An astronaut must feel like the feeling on a *roller coaster* as you *start down,* you get that *tingling feeling,* plus it's like maybe *driving a car for the first time, ice skating for the first time,* doing something you never did before."

## OSCAR

EARLIEST MEMORY—"Whenever I tell somebody this, they think I'm not telling the truth. *I can remember lying in a crib* watching my mother's shadow on the wall, the light would come through the doorway, that light could be off any room. The light would come through, and *she was walking back and forth going down the hall. I don't believe I could walk at that time."*

DREAMS—"The first nightmare I can remember is about a cat. I remember there was a *cat chasing* me around the block. I've had dreams where *somebody was chasing me* and I felt like I was *running on a treadmill* or in *deep sand, I couldn't get going.* I've had dreams where *I thought I could fly,* actually *fly, point myself in a direction.* Well, *I still have dreams like that,* mostly *over a desert,* or a wilderness, stream, or forest. *I can go anywhere* I want, *I'm actually flapping my arms,* I'm just like this [makes *flapping motion*]. I sort of *will myself* to *where I want to go.* I extend *my arms like wings,* sometimes if I want *altitude* I have to make *swimming motions. The last dream of this kind was a couple of weeks ago, may be a week ago.* I always had them, always had dreams like that."

SPORTS—"*I didn't take any part in sports at school,* I just felt trapped there."

MOTION—"*I spent all my time in my car.* I was in it constantly. I drove both when I was *upset* and when I was *calm.* It gave me a *sense of freedom. I hated to get up* in the morning. In the Marines *I started to fly,* and soloed in six hours. *I enjoyed it* very much, particularly the *freedom, being up there.* Once I got *away from the ground,* it was *like being in another world. Taking off,* there was a feeling of *anticipation* of it, getting *into the air, knowing what it was going to be like. I broke off from the ground.* Whenever *I was landing there was a little bit of tension,* the probability of *crashing.* It was a *feeling of well being, enjoying myself very much. Like going across the Pacific* on a troop ship, I used to get up on the deck, up front right behind the anchor chains and stay up there and *watch the bow crash* under the waves and throw spray. That's pretty much *like flying.* I used to have a *motorcycle* in California. I used to go *hill climbing,* pretty much the same thing, a *sense of freedom.* In Okinawa, I spent most of my time *skin diving.* I bought some flippers and face mask and every spare moment I had, I was down at the beach *diving in the coral. It was like flying,* like the *dreams of flying,* it's the same thing, because skin diving is *like flying, you can do barrel rolls* and everything else."

BODY SENSATIONS—"On the job it was like *in the Marines, run, run,* and then I took this *railroad* job and *laid around in bed for a couple of months. I didn't have any ambition.* I didn't want to do nothing. *I just didn't want to do anything.* I'm usually not that way. I had got on taking pills, *pep pills to get going* when I was working down at the station. During that time I would get *up in the morning* and take a pill and drink coffee or I would *go to sleep on the way to work.* I was *afraid* I was going to get killed. Then I would *fall asleep* on my way home so I would *take those pills to keep me going. Then I quit. I didn't do nothing* for about two months. *I couldn't move.* Then I got the job with the *railroad.* I think I pretty much *fell into a position where everything would be taken out of my hands and solved* for me. Everything for better or worse because it would be *out of my hands."*

# PHILIP

EARLIEST MEMORY—"It is when I was about six years old on a *tricycle.* I went *around the block.* It seemed an awful *long way.* I was kind of *scared,* wondering *if I would get back."*

DREAMS—*"Falling.* I had had that dream. *You just fall off a cliff* or something and *you wake up.* I don't know possibly it is *pretty far.* It wouldn't always be a *cliff.* Maybe one it would be *falling.* Another time I have had a dream before when *I tried to get enough strength to run or something and I couldn't* get enough *strength* and *I couldn't make my legs run fast enough.* My *body* would feel *heavy.* I would just *feel like I couldn't. I didn't have enough strength.* Then maybe it would be *fighting or something* like that. *The falling often would wake me up.* Lots of times like I mentioned *I couldn't run fast enough* But sometimes I would *start to run* and I would *have to leap up* in the air. *It was something like swimming.* I would have to make *my arms go* like this [patient makes *swimming motion*]. I would make a *long leap and then I would come down and each leap would be a little longer and I would start going up.* Then again I would have to *fight pretty hard to get up* in the air. I mean I would have to *make my arms* pretty, well, *I'm showing you.* But then one time *I got up too high* and I *got scared so I came down.* It seemed like I was up *above the telephone poles.* I got up *too high.* Then I *came down.* Then I *woke up. This dream is better, better to get away from something.* My feelings actually *change.* It's the *feeling of getting away,* being loose from. *Nothing can hold you down.* This is what the feeling is. On the other hand *being held down* is like being dead—a nightmare. I feel *trapped* when I am in prison."

SPORTS—"I didn't have *nothing to do with sports.* I was *skipping school* at the time."

MOTION—*"Flying, it is like beautiful.* When I *put my head back* and feel the plane *take off, it is like leaving everything.* It is like a *new beginning, like starting, like leaving things behind.* Time is funny, *it goes the same and yet it seems to go slower,* like being a child *waiting* for Christmas. *In my job of forging* I have *moved all around* the country, *at least 100,000 miles in the last five years. I would take and work the country up into sections.* I'd go to California, Canada, Mexico. Gambling, I'd go to Vegas. I would work all of California for a while and I would try to *go then to some place that I hadn't been* in two or three years. A lot of times I also *drove my own car. I spent hundreds of dollars on taxicabs just riding around when I hadn't rented a car.* The first time I *flew* was at sixteen going *back home* sort of for a *reunion.* I would feel a lot *better on a jet if I were coming home for a reunion,* say, than if you were on a *jet going.* . . . I was anxious *to get out of there* so I just got to thinking of it as a *reunion* even though I was just *gone just a short* while. Well it is about a two-hour flight. Depends, non-stop *you sit back and have a drink* and then an hour later you *land in New York, the weather is different and everything.* It feels like you are *leaving your* problems behind—not really but it gives you *that feeling.* I would like to be *an astronaut.* It would be *an elated feeling,* one of the most *elated feelings* you could have, *be over the whole earth,* feeling that most of us being a little *lost.* Be very *difficult to tell things from up there.* I wouldn't mind at all."

BODY SENSATIONS—"When I was in this *prison* before I went up on the *watertower* and *I stood up there* and *told them I was going to fly.* Well, that wasn't my intent. I wasn't thinking of *flying away. I was putting on an act.* I had to *look for a pattern.* After I got down I had to draw things, *things that could fly, that in reality couldn't.* I drew a picture of some kind of an animal and put long hair on one side of it *tearing itself apart. It was divided down the middle. At times I felt divided down the middle.* I felt that *in the morning I would feel different than at night,* and I would feel *divided* in this way. I would *want to do something* and I would *change my mind and feel the complete reverse of it,* complete *opposite.* I feel *more at peace at night* than I do in the *mornings. I wasn't thinking of flying away when I jumped out of a jail window* after I was busted. A guy would *have to be crazy to think like that.*"

# RONALD

EARLIEST MEMORY—"I guess the only recollection I do have is *playing out in the yard,* you know, riding a *tricycle* and *stuff like that.*"

DREAMS—"It was something about me and the devil. The devil was chasing me around."

SPORTS—"I *lettered* in football, played basketball in junior college. Never did care for baseball too much."

MOVEMENT—"*I started parachute jumping at thirty-two years of age.* I took him [my friend] out to the *airport* to go back to Vietnam. I said *I felt like I was in the Salvation Army.* I've seen so many *come and go.* I felt like *I wanted to go with him* and then *I would get upset* and I would *just walk outside and I would walk for a long time.* At Cuba I think I did say, 'I hate for you all to have *to land,* if you could just pop across there and *if I had a chute I would just go* out.' This conversation—'they' said I was going to *jump* out of the airplane. If I had a *chute* I might have, but I didn't. Then *things started moving kind of fast. I wanted to jump out* of the plane while it was still *rolling.*"


## RAFE

DREAMS—"The major dream I have, I told the other doctors this. I have a *pistol* and somebody else has a *pistol.* I don't know who it is. *I try to fire* at them and they fire at me and a woman *jumps* in the middle. I don't know any of the other people. The trigger on the gun, *I can't pull it* or else I pull it and *it won't go off. My hands feel heavy. Everything I do is heavy in a dream.* I don't know what happens to her. It *stops* right there. In a lot of ways it is *just like slow motion.* As a kid in dreams I would be either *being chased.* I was *trying to stop somebody* from doing something and *I could never quite . . . the dream has never ended.* There is *no conclusion in a dream.* It takes different *forms.* It is not always the same dream. *I am one of two people,* the other person is getting me or I'm getting them—a *lot of upstairs and downstairs* and I have the *sensation* sometimes—I will be in the middle of a dream and *I will fall downstairs, a sense of falling.* I will be *lying perfectly normal, like this, in my bed and have the same thing happen to me.* It even *happens to me as an adult.* You know *your leg twitches if you miss a step going up stairs. This will happen to me when I am awake,* reading a book or something, but it has *no relationship to the book.*"

SPORTS—"I *didn't play any games.* I didn't have any friends. The only time my daddy ever hurt me I was about eleven. He wanted me to go over and play baseball at a bunch of kids and *I didn't want to go play baseball* with them. I just didn't want to go play baseball. He really got harsh, 'Well, get to hell over there and play baseball. What's the matter, are you a sissy or something?' I am a *lousy runner. I'm a joke running around.*"

MOTION—"I've travelled *at least 200,000 miles by airplane* in the last couple of years and *probably half that much in cars.* When I am *really upset I get in the car and drive and drive and drive.* One time I drove from *Houston* and *then repeated that same trip three more times before I cooled off.* As a teenager when *I got really confused,* sometime*s I would drive for a week or longer never even know where I had been.* I would *come to myself* way the hell out in Houston or someplace. I've had some *training as a pilot,* but I don't have a license. I often *wonder if I am crazy,* but I sit in my cell and I get so bored and *I'll do this you know, maneuvers of an aircraft. You know, with my hands.* I don't give a damn if these other guys are watching me or not—*approaches and takeoffs— I'll do it with my hands* because I have nothing else to do. *I intended to be a parachutist* in the Army."

# GLADYS

EARLIEST MEMORY—"I remember *dropping* and breaking my father's red phonograph record. I broke it one day. My other memory, *I fell down the cellar stairs.* I came *up the stairs* from the cellar and couldn't get the door open. I just couldn't get the door open and I was pushing real hard and I just *fell. I fell backwards all the way down,* but I went unconscious before I hit."

DREAMS—"Oh, you mean my dreams. I will tell you my dreams. I am *flying.* I am able to *fly* and I am *flying* and *flying* and *flying, without weight, just flying, man, just me flying.* There are people tangled up in telephone wires and I can't go by *without getting them free.* I have to let them free you know, they are *all tangled up* so *I free them.* There are hundreds of people—big chore. Then I see a whole crowd of people who look exactly like my mother *standing on the ground,* they are facing up to me and I say, 'Who is my mother?' and they all say 'I am,' every single one of them. I say 'Wow.' I am *flying through them* and there are a whole bunch of people and every single one of them looks like my brother and I say 'Who is my brother?' and they all say 'I am,' and *I am flying* and I see a whole crowd of people that look exactly like my father and I say 'Who is my father?' and they all say 'I am.' I go back home and I go into the kitchen and there is just three witches with black pointed hats, black costumes *but no brooms.* I never thought about whether those witches could *fly* or not. *I never saw those witches fly.* My witches never *fly.* I used to have a kind of *masochistic fantasy* with my witches. They did some of the wildest things to people and me included. They would *pounce on me* and *put me in a typewriter* and type on me. They would *make a lampshade out of me. They would use me for a mattress,* me and others. Oh, they were wild, they were the wildest witches. I had them for the longest time until maybe twelve or so. *I often felt very flat.* I mostly *felt flat most of the time.* They used to use me for *rugs* and stuff, use you like a *piece of paper* or something. Those witches and they all have the *hats.* In those fantasies, *especially when I was a mattress I could feel my body change.* I think I really enjoyed that, *being a mattress.* The witches would ċome and *lie on you,* you were a *mattress.* But the dreams, the *dreams of flying. That was my bag.* Those dreams started like after the ones I had being *chased on the school grounds by a big monster and not being able to get up in the air but you know you can fly* [laughter], *but you can't get started. You can't get off the ground.* When *I couldn't get off the ground,* the feeling was that of *frustration. I would feel paralyzed.* Those are the only two dreams I am really with. *The paralyzed dreams don't happen as often as my flying dreams.* I call it my *flying dream. I used to have it almost all the time, but I don't anymore.* Probably the last one was when I was about *fifteen.*"

MOVEMENT—"When I was a kid and taking *ballet I used to try to jump in the air and stay without coming down. I jumped higher and higher.* It was *beautiful flight.* It was a *beautiful flight.* He was a *wonderful pilot*. He really did *pilot well*. Other than it was *beautiful;* I felt *elated* [patient *extends arm as if in flight*]. It is *like flying*. I feel like I can *experience it* all again. Yes, that is what it was. It was the *plane*. *Those are my arms,* oh yes, it was really *nice*. *My brother is afraid of heights*. You know what I really would like to do? *Parachute, skydive*. I've always wanted to and *I've always wanted to kill myself by jumping*. *Skydiving must be like a pre-orgastic dream* you have when you *fall* and then you *jerk,* you know. It must be like that in the *dream*. You are getting pretty near to health, but you are not all the way there. You aren't really ready to have orgasm, healthy orgasm, but you are *getting there* and this is why you *jerk* and *wake up*. *At night when you are asleep and you are falling and you wake like* . . . it must be *like your body is bathed in realness*. It is not like your body is *just walking around lost, meaningless, and your mind is busy*. Well, it *will be the air rushing,* but there will be so *many openings,* if they *will open*. You know what I mean? Like if you *spread out* completely you would be just completely open. Well, see, *I'm not reality oriented*. There are orgones and energy and orgone energy. Like there is heat, the energy of heat. This is like life. Orgone energy is like life. It is like *life energy* and you have it. People have orgone energy. That is the stuff of which . . . when you *cut it off* you armor it, muscle it. Then man you are fucked up! Then you have deadly *orgone energy and it is all stale* and it is just Blam. It is bad stuff. *You have to break through it. You have to force it through* whatever armor you have and usually *you have rings of armor going around* your body at various places, different places to help it. Mostly stomach, chest, eyes, face, the whole thing, and *you have to keep breaking through it; breaking through it from the top* probably *going down* toward the pelvis. *It is like with a baby after it is born*. It has to *break through the rings of paralysis*. Oh, *I am anti-gravity. I took ballet lessons*. I *danced* for a couple of years, more than that, three or four years. Now, *that is what you want. You fill yourself up with air and the sensation of flying is such a thing I was after. I would jump and try to defy it*. I used to *try to keep on jumping,* but I didn't know. I never thought about it. To me the major feelings was the *freeness,* the *freeness of it, trying to get free,* but it is like waves, see. Most people are like this chronically [shows me a *clinched hand* and *then an open hand*] of healthy things like that. You can be *open* or you can be *closed.* You can be *armored* when you have to be or you can be *unarmored.* You are not *trapped in your armor* or completely without *armor. You can move.* See? *Without your armor you can practically fly.* Men had always been *trying to fly all their lives,* jumping off *cliffs* with straw *wings.* I feel that George's *spirit and mine know how to fly and meet. I feel like I am not here,* he's not there and I'm not there and he's not here. We've met *someplace in nil,* like I'm not afraid of *losing* him. We just 'zonk'—like that. *I know all of this is not a dream because it doesn't end.* It has *lasted* so long, but that is the way I know. *My body feels like nothing.* It is sad. It is *meaningless.* I'm *not even aware of my body very much. I'm above it,* always above it, *although I feel it could float,* particularly if I am *at the top* of a head of *stairs. As a child I was always afraid to get very high. I couldn't control the position of my body.* I was *afraid. Movement, it has always been a force.* It has had to be a *force* for me. Just the fear of *breaking through,* the unwillingness to *break through* the rings. You see your *armoring is not irrational, it is custom made. You came up with it* yourself during your life to suit your own needs and you are fond of it. You need it. Oh God, do you need it. It is like your favorite suit, your only suit and you are having to tear it to shreds and it hurts. *Prison* is a whole new thing, man, just a wild new thing. The *weight,* the *sadness,* everybody has it. You should look in the eyes of people who are in *prison.*

"At the fair wow, I like the *whip.* Then there were some of those *high rides.* Oh, I used to love those. Oh, *wow,* like the *swings* that go around, *higher, higher.* You know the *centrifugal force* takes you out like this. You are *swinging* around. It is *beautiful.* I *en-joyed* that. I enjoyed those *rides.* On the *roller coaster*—now you are *scared.* You get in and it is sunny and *it is right now.* You get *locked in* with a bar and it is beginning way back on the *edge,* now you are *rocking* back and forth way on the *edge.* This thing is right here and you are *holding on to it* and you are *looking down.* The *thing about a roller coaster is the falling.* You don't *zoom* up. You *crawl up* and then you *zoom down* and you are *crawling up* and you want to *go up. You want the thing to go even higher.* You are *leaning forward* and everything is kind of *behind you.* You are *leaning forward* and you *get to the top* and there is just a moment. *The sun is up there* and you can see the whole fair if you're looking, but really you are not because you are just on the *very, very top.* You suck in your *breath,* yeah, you do because then [laugh] you are *like a bullet going down.* I think the *best part is when you are on the very top and you know you are going to zoom down,* but you haven't done it yet. You are just *right up there,* you know. It is just like sometimes when you get to the *top* of the ferris wheel and it *stops* and sometimes you are *way up there.* You know. You're at the *very top* and *you want it to go farther* but it won't, and you know that's it. You are *right there* and when it *hits the bottom, oh wow, falling, you are falling.* You know you are not really on the *roller coaster,* but you can hear the sound of people *screaming.* I think that you are *screaming* too. I think that I scream too, *but I am not making any noise.* You really are, you really are going to be *completely into the ground.* You know like there isn't any tracks anymore, *but you can't fight it.* Like you've already *gone to the top,* now you are *going down, like you want to go down.* You want to go *completely down.* You are *going down* at the very *last moment. They save you* and *you go* through the whole thing again. The way you feel when you *come back down* and the people who weren't on the ride with you and the *people who were down on the ground. Just mortals, they were so little.* They are so *little* when you look at them. You come on *back down, down, down* and the steps made of wood make some noises and a man helps you out and you are going *down, down, down* and you know it is where you were before, but you went on the ride you know—big thing.

"*Time—time is joke to me. It doesn't run the same length all the time. In death I would like to fly straight out into* the arms of the *stars* into the night and feel myself come *thinner* and *thinner like cigarette smoke until I was in the stars and the night.* You know, so maybe I was like one of them. On our second acid trip we took some more and he was wearing this purple shirt and he was completely purple. Well, you know what I mean, *on acid you feel like you are just geographically going somewhere* as well because you got to look at things fifteen times, right. Geographically you might. I would think, 'Wow, *how far am I going into this land?' Actually* moving, then when it's done how can I ever fit in with the world again? When we were out in the country and behind a house, it had a hill and we went to the fence and everybody down at the house was getting high, but he said, 'Come on, we have to go.' Yes, we have to go. *We have to get out of this world. We have to go,* and I was just the tiniest bit afraid, but he was so intent on going. *We had to go.* So I said okay, so we *crawled,* under the fence and we *got to the top* of the hill and *I said 'Can we actually fly now?' 'Can we actually jump off this world?'* He said, 'Sure we can.' *So we kind of like jumped off the world.* Then we couldn't get *back down* off the hill. We couldn't get *back down smaller again* because we wouldn't *find our way. We couldn't find it. There was no weight.* We were just *going to go off the world,* and I was a little bit *afraid,* but I said, 'Okay, *let's go off the world.'* Our bodies had *changed shape as well as weight. That happens too when you are just generally elated."*

## GEORGE

DREAMS—"I think I used to dream about *floating,* generally a very *up feeling, drifting over landscapes.* For some reason *there is always a corner block.* It wasn't near where I lived, it was on the corner where there is this *vacant building. There is a brook* there and I used to think that was the place I was *drifting.* I think I pretty much *drifted around* and *wasn't in control of my own motions. I don't remember ever taking off.* Usually there was a kind of grid thing, brown dried grass. I remember it was *exciting, very. Totally different from how I felt when I was awake.* One time I *dreamed of being dead.* I felt kind of good because I *was separated from everything.* I was kind of an *observer.* I can't remember what my parents thought. I can remember the general idea."

BODY SENSATIONS—"*The daytime feelings of my body was a whole different experience. My whole body felt different. In the dreams* to real life, but *when I was dreaming I really felt how good it was.* About life—I don't know. I guess it just makes you feel *trapped.* When you are *in the air* that is the *direction you can take and how fast you can move. When you are on the ground you are limited.* In my daydreams I think *excitement* was the big thing with me because I remember *in the pantomime of the baseball game there was always* a lot of *excitement* and *tension* and the *crowd going crazy.* I don't *feel any identification with a car. I still can't drive a car. When I turn the wheel to back up I always get confused.* You *turn the wheel one way* and the car goes the other way. You *turn the wheel this way* and you go like that and it is *supposed to go in like that but it always goes wrong.* The *rides out at the fairgrounds make me feel* very tense, *clampish,* particularly *those that went around.* In cars with other fellows I wouldn't be happy. I would get nervous, but then I would say to hell with it. One girl I used to have sex with was kind of a slop through the *mud, quagmire,* cloudy, *type of thing.* That is the way it seemed. When I started smoking grass I remember getting a *little feeling* and of a *step ladder going down.* I think that on grass *you go up* and then *you look down* from the *ladders* and you can see things *in the order they occur* in your life. In the order of importance, like on a *level.* You would probably be on the *first level* and the second might be life and the *third level* might be the tape recorder. *On grass it is not like rising or flying, it is more a floating feeling.* You feel *your body going through the levels* of priority. *In life I was just going through the motions* of what I was doing because I had no idea of what else I could do. Just one time I got in a fight. I felt completely like a machine. Like I *had no feelings* whatsoever. This was just an operation I was to perform. Afterwards I had the *most incredible tightness and stiffness in my whole body and I felt myself completely rigid.* It took me at least three or four days *to even feel* a little—you know a complete tenseness over my whole body, fantastic. I felt *brittle, ready to break,* like *if I put my hand out* it would shatter all sharpness. *On acid maybe I thought I could leap out into space.* I think so. But *distance and the patterns* of the other feels almost like a painting. I think we even discussed *walking.* I don't recall *jumping* or feeling like if I could *drop* over into the next field *a lot of anxiety of going back where we had come from.* In a *high place* I always feel *my body wanting to go over.* When the *plane took off* I was really surprised at the *speed* and the *way it went up* like that. In *flying* it is kind of a *surging upward* and a *gradual softening downward.* It had just come to a place, where for myself it was time for me to do something. Here I had been for *twenty-one years just floating through the world, walking around blah, blah, not really getting anywhere,* making any kind of decision, *not taking any kind of stand*—a kind of follow the leader thing. At a time like that I think a fellow has *broken the chain,* either a real chain or a figurative chain. I think that is good for people. I think it is *dangerous* for people to break out, but I think it is necessary. A chain is kind of a *habitual low-energy living.* Each day just *breathing just enough to get enough oxygen to be able to move around.* You are always kind of *blah.* I am that way, a *very stagnant* kind of person. *Life is heavy, kind of dragging around.* I think it is very *very tiring.* In the same environment anything will irritate you. You begin to breathe deeply and to live on a *higher energy level and you can get excited about things.* You surround yourself with all kinds of things that are really *tied around your waist. When you break the chains you get free of a lot of things that are encumbering.* Then on the plain *I just rose up and walked through the curtain.* I just *wanted to make* a change, a different way of living, a *comfortable functioning,* you know. I had *low* energy level just *dragging through.* I just really feel *upset* with myself about being so *lethargic* most of the time. It was only once a week or once a month that I would say, 'Oh, my God, why even be alive?' I would see that after a few more years of this that maybe there would *never be a future.* You know, *try to shake myself loose.* It started in high school. I first began to notice it. I don't know how long I had been doing it. I would come home from school and *lie down and go to sleep* to six o'clock and then *get up,* eat supper and *go sit and watch TV* until ten and then go upstairs and *go to bed* and *feel tired in the morning,* and *skip school. Sometimes my body feels far away.* It *hardly ever feels a part of me* now in prison. Just feels like *living by itself,* keeping itself alive *without any cooperation* between myself and it. This *separation* began about two months ago when I began to feel a *clear headedness. When I sit down* at my bunk or something I just can't think of anything. I look at light and I try to figure out what I would like to think about it and figure *how it is coming through the window.* Why it is making that shadow. It is such a smooth, smooth surface. There is nothing there. I think a lot of guys in here are operating at *low energy levels.* I feel in many ways *I am not capable of functioning.* In many ways I allow myself to be a *lot weaker* because of a *lack of determination, lack of direction, a general fear of asserting* myself. I think   Gladys *acts as a catalyst for me.* She gets me moving, not necessarily in the direction of success, but *she prods* me onward. *I usually go in spurts.* I go for a week *lying around* and then go into a *spurt* thing. I think I have always worked that way. I would go *two or three weeks without doing anything* and spend a *week catching up*—things like that."

## TED

EARLIEST MEMORIES—Involve the *death* of both parents. The mother when he was five and the father at six.

DREAMS—"There are no dreams that I can recall that happen over and over at night. Of course, I thought about mom and dad quite often, but as far as dreams I don't think so. I can remember a *couple of dreams of falling,* more or less I would be *just dozing off* in a dream and fall as if you would be *falling* and I would *jump back.* I guess mostly I dreamed about *outdoors,* playing things in life, similar to that. I do care a lot about the *outdoors.* I never liked geography tests, I felt sort of *trapped.* I like to be *outside* in the fresh air in the country. Here in *prison I fall asleep* and *just let my mind wander off. It goes outside.* What I could do after I do *get out."*

SPORTS—"I played *baseball and basketball and track.* I made the team. I played for the high school I went to. I played in the Army. My *coordination is pretty good.* In *parachute jumping* I never got hurt once."

MOVEMENT—"I planned to take *flying lessons* when I got out of the Army, and I was also thinking about going into skydiving. While I'm here in prison I'll get mad, but once I leave here and get out to where I'm going, I'll have a chance to *get out and walk. Walk it all off.* That's the way I work things out [walking], or by *driving a car,* usually. I do that pretty much. When I was about ten or eleven, I couldn't *ride in a car* for more than about an hour and a half and then *I would vomit.* Then have some Pepto Bismol or something. I used to get sick on board ship, too, when I was older, but that was always from watching somebody else get sick.

"At the time of the divorce the *judge just let everything fall from my hands.* The kids—I wanted to *hand them* everything—everything I didn't have because I didn't have parents. I wanted to be double good to those two."

## WILL

EARLIEST MEMORIES—Other than an early sexual memory involving a little boy and a little girl, memories are these: "Well, there used to be a building contractor. He had a lot across from these stables where he stored his wagon. They didn't have trucks in them days. I remember there was one truck that was turned upside down and I used to get a *big thrill* by going to that lot and getting on the large hind wheel and *wrapping my body sort of around the hub and spinning on it.* I don't know whether anyone else ever saw me, but *I often used to do that.* I spent a lot of time *spinning on that wheel.* I got a *big thrill* out of that. Another thing, my mother used to deal at a little store and she used to send me after 2 cents of skim milk in a little can about that big around and it had a tall tail on it with a wire handle, and when I came back from the store I would be *swinging* that can around like this [*makes rotary motion*]. You know, but I *never spilled any of it.* I was pretty good at that. It was a *big thrill because I was in the middle.*"

MOVEMENT—"My shoe laces become tied overnight or my socks tied in knots, or *mustard falls* as evidence of the physical presence of my father who would play that kind of joke."

# SUMMARY

Undoubtedly, even with the use of italics to cause parts of speech to stand out, the content of their communication will lack some of the vibrant quality heard when one is part of the interview.

Some of the statements represent "hard signs" of vestibular pathology, others "soft signs," and others "interpretive content." To avoid misunderstanding, let me say that I am well aware of the fact that one can exist in time and space without the inner ear. Sufferers from Ménière's Syndrome celebrate the day that surgical ablation of the organ was attempted. (I might add that some hellish and untreatable depressions disappeared with the affected organ.) As long as one has any two of his three basic spatial systems working in good condition, one can afford the loss of the third without serious problem. The three are the eyes, the ears, and the proprioceptors. The absence of one is tolerable. But is a serious malfunction of one tolerable? The answer to this question is clearly "No." Normal inputs from two or three of the systems can be handled by the structure of the floor of the fourth ventricle, but it cannot but fall into spatial disorganization and emotional disequilibrium in its incapacity to handle normal inputs from two systems and non-concordant impulses from the third.

It is my contention that the deeply buried inner ear is primary in the triad and so physiologically fluctuant that its changes in function produce "in depth" changes in affect and orientation, even in normal individuals. At such moments, transient signs come and go. In more serious and chronic disturbance, the whole personality undergoes more or less chronic change.

The clinical material suggests a range of acute and chronic dysfunction and non-concordance of inputs from the rest of the body (eye and proprioceptor) with the vestibulum, resulting in psychic anxiety and confusion. The afflicted person tries to solve these geographically, posturally, and affectively, by thought and delusion. In the process, there follows an overall developmental sequence and an ultimate infirmity, which becomes recognizable when studied in cross-section.

# Appendix B

## MASTER LIST OF ALL HIJACKING ATTEMPTS
### UPDATED JULY 29, 1970
### WORLDWIDE, AIR CARRIER AND GENERAL AVIATION

The following list is based upon a comprehensive survey of hijacking events from the files of the Federal Aviation Administration, the Department of State, International Air Transport Association as well as files of a number of newspapers and periodicals. The list does not include theft of aircraft or the hijacking of military aircraft.

### Number Code

First 3 digits are the serial number of the hijacking attempt

Next 6 digits are month, day and year

Next 2 digits represent the country owning aircraft

Next to last digit is 1 for successful attempt and 0 for unsuccessful attempt

Last digit is 1 for air carrier and 0 for general aviation

### Country Code

| | | | |
|---|---|---|---|
| 0 Other | 16 USSR | 24 Turkey | 39 E. Germany |
| 1 USA | 17 Czechoslovakia | 25 Rumania | 40 Japan |
| 2 Cuba | 18 Greece | 26 Yugoslavia | 41 British Honduras |
| 3 Colombia | 19 Israel | 27 Bulgaria | 42 Trinidad |
| 4 Venezuela | 20 Egypt | 28 Poland | 43 Italy |
| 5 Ecuador | 21 Ethiopia | 29 South Korea | 44 Iran |
| 6 Peru | 22 Nigeria | 30 France | 45 Saudi Arabia |
| 7 Argentina | 23 Honduras | 31 Hong Kong | |
| 8 Nicaragua | | 32 Brazil | |
| 9 Mexico | | 33 Haiti | |
| 10 Canada | | 34 Chile | |
| 11 U.K. | | 35 Costa Rica | |
| 12 Netherlands | | 36 Spain | |
| 13 Portugal | | 37 Panama | |
| 14 Australia | | 38 Curacao | |
| 15 Philippines | | | |

# MASTER LIST OF ALL HIJACKING ATTEMPTS—WORLDWIDE, AIR CARRIER AND GENERAL AVIATION

| | | | |
|---|---|---|---|
| 001 | (1930) | 0611 | Peru/Peru |
| 002 | 072547 | 2510 | Rumania/Turkey |
| 003 | 040848 | 1711 | Czechoslovakia/US Zone Germany |
| 004 | 050448 | 1711 | Czechoslovakia/US Zone Germany |
| 005 | 060448 | 2611 | Yugoslavia/Italy |
| 006 | 061748 | 2511 | Rumania/Austria |
| 007 | 063048 | 2711 | Bulgaria/Turkey |
| 008 | 071648 | 3101 | Hong Kong/Unknown |
| 009 | 091248 | 1811 | Greece/Yugoslavia |
| 010 | 042949 | 2511 | Rumania/Greece |
| 011 | 120949 | 2511 | Rumania/Yugoslavia |
| 012 | 121649 | 2811 | Poland/Denmark |
| 013 | 032450 | 1711 | Czechoslovakia/US Zone Germany |
| 014 | 032450 | 1711 | Czechoslovakia/US Zone Germany |
| 015 | 032450 | 1711 | Czechoslovakia/US Zone Germany |
| 016 | 123052 | 1501 | Philippines/Red China |
| 017 | 032353 | 1711 | Czechoslovakia/West Germany |
| 018 | 021658 | 2911 | South Korea/North Korea |
| 019 | 041058 | 2901 | South Korea/North Korea |
| 020 | 102258 | 0201 | Cuba/Cuba |
| 021 | 110158 | 0201 | Cuba/Cuba |
| 022 | 110658 | 0211 | Cuba/Cuba |
| 023 | 041659 | 0211 | Cuba/USA |
| 024 | 041059 | 3311 | Haiti/Cuba |
| 025 | 100259 | 0211 | Cuba/USA |
| 026 | 041260 | 0211 | Cuba/USA |
| 027 | 070560 | 0211 | Cuba/USA |
| 028 | 071860 | 0211 | Cuba/Jamaica |
| 029 | 071960 | 1401 | Australia/Singapore |
| 030 | 072860 | 0211 | Cuba/USA |
| 031 | 082160 | 1601 | USSR/Unknown |
| 032 | 102960 | 0211 | Cuba/USA |
| 033 | 120860 | 0201 | Cuba/USA |
| 034 | 050161 | 0111 | USA/Cuba NAL |
| 035 | 070361 | 0211 | Cuba/USA |
| 036 | 072461 | 0111 | USA/Cuba EAL |
| 037 | 073161 | 0101 | USA/USA PAC |
| 038 | 080361 | 0101 | USA/Cuba CAL |
| 039 | 080961 | 0111 | USA/Cuba PAA |
| 040 | 080961 | 0201 | Cuba/USA |
| 041 | 091061 | 1600 | USSR/Armenia |
| 042 | 110611 | 1311 | Portugal/Spanish Morocco |
| 043 | 112761 | 0411 | Venezuela/Netherlands Antilles |
| 044 | 031762 | 3001 | France/France |
| 045 | 041362 | 0110 | USA/Cuba |
| 046 | 041662 | 1201 | Netherlands/East Germany |
| 047 | 080563 | 0100 | USA/Cuba |
| 048 | 112863 | 0411 | Venezuela/Trinidad |
| 049 | 021864 | 0110 | USA/Cuba |
| 050 | 101964 | 1601 | USSR/Unknown |

| | | | | | | | |
|---|---|---|---|---|---|---|---|
| 051 | Spring '65 | 1601 | USSR/Unknown | 080 | 071768 | 0111 | USA/Cuba NAL |
| 052 | 083165 | 0111 | USA/USA HAW AL | 081 | 072368 | 1911 | Israel/Algeria |
| 053 | 101165 | 0101 | USA/USA ALOHA AL | 082 | 080468 | 0110 | USA/Cuba |
| 054 | 102665 | 0101 | USA/Cuba NAL | 083 | 082268 | 0110 | USA/Cuba |
| 055 | 111765 | 0101 | USA/Cuba NAL | 084 | 091168 | 1001 | Canada/Cuba |
| 056 | 032766 | 0201 | Cuba/USA | 085 | 092068 | 0111 | USA/Cuba EAL |
| 057 | Spring '66 | 1601 | USSR/Turkey | 086 | 092268 | 0311 | Colombia/Cuba |
| 058 | 070766 | 0211 | Cuba/Jamaica | 087 | 092268 | 0311 | Colombia/Cuba |
| 059 | 080966 | 1601 | USSR/Turkey | 088 | 100668 | 0911 | Mexico/Cuba |
| 060 | 092866 | 0711 | Argentina/Falkland Islands | 089 | 102368 | 0110 | USA/Cuba |
| 061 | 020767 | 2011 | Egypt/Jordan | 090 | 103068 | 0911 | Mexico/USA |
| 062 | 042367 | 2211 | Nigeria/Nigeria | 091 | 110268 | 0101 | USA/Cuba EAL |
| 063 | 063067 | 1110 | United Kingdom/Algeria | 092 | 110468 | 0111 | USA/Cuba NAL |
| 064 | 080667 | 0311 | Colombia/Cuba | 093 | 110668 | 1511 | Philippines/Philippines |
| 065 | 090967 | 0311 | Colombia/Cuba | 094 | 110868 | 1811 | Greece/Greece |
| 066 | 112067 | 0101 | USA/Cuba | 095 | 111868 | 0911 | Mexico/Cuba |
| 067 | 020968 | 0101 | USA/Hong Kong PAA | 096 | 112368 | 0111 | USA/Cuba EAL |
| 068 | 021768 | 0110 | USA/Cuba | 097 | 112468 | 0111 | USA/Cuba PAA |
| 069 | 022168 | 0111 | USA/Cuba Delta | 098 | 113068 | 0111 | USA/Cuba EAL |
| 070 | 030568 | 0311 | Colombia/Cuba | 099 | 120368 | 0111 | USA/Cuba NAL |
| 071 | 031268 | 0111 | USA/Cuba NAL | 100 | 121168 | 0111 | USA/Cuba TWA |
| 072 | 031668 | 0910 | Mexico/Cuba | 101 | 121968 | 0111 | USA/Cuba EAL |
| 073 | 032268 | 0411 | Venezuela/Cuba | 102 | 010269 | 0111 | USA/Cuba EAL |
| 074 | 061968 | 0411 | Venezuela/Cuba | 103 | 010269 | 1811 | Greece/Egypt |
| 075 | 062968 | 0111 | USA/Cuba Southeast AL | 104 | 010769 | 0311 | Colombia/Cuba |
| 076 | 070168 | 0111 | USA/Cuba NW | 105 | 010969 | 0111 | USA/Cuba EAL |
| 077 | 070468 | 0101 | USA/Mexico TWA | 106 | 011169 | 0111 | USA/Cuba UAL |
| 078 | 071268 | 0110 | USA/Cuba | 107 | 011169 | 0611 | Peru/Cuba |
| 079 | 071268 | 0101 | USA/Cuba Delta | 108 | 011369 | 0101 | USA/Cuba Delta |

| | | | |
|---|---|---|---|
| 109 | 011969 | 0III | USA/Cuba EAL |
| 110 | 011969 | 05II | Ecuador/Cuba |
| 111 | 012469 | 0III | USA/Cuba NAL |
| 112 | 012869 | 0III | USA/Cuba NAL |
| 113 | 012869 | 0III | USA/Cuba EAL |
| 114 | 013169 | 0III | USA/Cuba NAL |
| 115 | 020369 | 0III | USA/Cuba EAL |
| 116 | 020369 | 0I0I | USA/Cuba NAL |
| 117 | 020569 | 03II | Colombia/Cuba |
| 118 | 020869 | 090I | Mexico/Cuba |
| 119 | 021069 | 0III | USA/Cuba EAL |
| 120 | 021169 | 04II | Venezuela/Cuba |
| 121 | 022569 | 0III | USA/Cuba EAL |
| 122 | 030569 | 0III | USA/Cuba NAL |
| 123 | 031169 | 030I | Colombia/Cuba |
| 124 | 031569 | 03II | Colombia/Cuba |
| 125 | 031769 | 06II | Peru/Cuba |
| 126 | 031769 | 0III | USA/Cuba Delta |
| 127 | 031969 | 0I0I | USA/Cuba Delta |
| 128 | 032569 | 0III | USA/Cuba Delta |
| 129 | 041169 | 05II | Ecuador/Cuba |
| 130 | 041369 | 0III | USA/Cuba PAA |
| 131 | 041469 | 03II | Colombia/Cuba |
| 132* | | | |
| 133 | 050569 | 0III | USA/Cuba NAL |
| 134 | 052069 | 03II | Colombia/Cuba |
| 135 | 052669 | 0III | USA/Cuba NE |
| 136 | 053069 | 0I0I | USA/Cuba Tex. Int. |
| 137 | 060469 | 13II | Portugal/Congo |
| 138 | 061769 | 0III | USA/Cuba TWA |
| 139 | 062069 | 03II | Colombia/Cuba |
| 140 | 062269 | 0III | USA/Cuba EAL |
| 141 | 062569 | 0III | USA/Cuba UAL |
| 142 | 062869 | 0III | USA/Cuba EAL |
| 143 | 070369 | 05II | Ecuador/Cuba |
| 144 | 071069 | 030I | Colombia/Cuba |
| 145 | 072669 | 0III | USA/Cuba CAL |
| 146 | 072669 | 09II | Mexico/Cuba |
| 147 | 072969 | 090I | Nicaragua/Cuba |
| 148 | 073169 | 0III | USA/Cuba TWA |
| 149 | 080469 | 03II | Colombia/Cuba |
| 150 | 080569 | 0I0I | USA/Cuba EAL |
| 151 | 081269 | 2III | Ethiopia/Sudan |
| 152 | 081469 | 0III | USA/Cuba NE |
| 153 | 081669 | 18II | Greece/Albania |
| 154 | 081869 | 20II | Egypt/Saudi Arabia |
| 155 | 082369 | 03II | Colombia/Cuba |
| 156 | 082969 | 0III | USA/Cuba NAL |
| 157 | 082969 | 0III | USA/Syria TWA |
| 158 | 090669 | 05II | Ecuador/Cuba |
| 159 | 090669 | 050I | Ecuador/Cuba |
| 160 | 090769 | 0III | USA/Cuba EAL |
| 161 | 091069 | 0I0I | USA/Cuba EAL |
| 162 | 091369 | 2III | Ethiopia/S. Yemen Republic |
| 163 | 091369 | 23II | Honduras/San Salvador |
| 164 | 091669 | 24II | Turkey/Bulgaria |
| 165 | 092469 | 0III | USA/Cuba NAL |
| 166 | 100869 | 32II | Brazil/Cuba |

...of insufficient evidence. It has been determined not to be an offense covered by

| No. | Date | Code | Route |
|---|---|---|---|
| 167 | 100869 | 0711 | Argentina/Cuba |
| 168 | 100969 | 0111 | USA/Cuba NAL |
| 169 | 101969 | 2811 | Poland/W. Berlin (French) |
| 170 | 102169 | 0111 | USA/Cuba (Mex. C.-Merida) PAA |
| 171 | 102869 | 0311 | Colombia/Cuba |
| 172 | 103169 | 0111 | USA/Italy (Rome) TWA |
| 173 | 110469 | 0811 | Nicaragua/Cuba |
| 174 | 110469 | 3211 | Brazil/Cuba |
| 175 | 110869 | 0701 | Argentina/Cuba |
| 176 | 111069 | 0101 | USA/(Sweden, Mexico or Brazil) DL |
| 177 | 111269 | 3401 | Chile/Cuba |
| 178 | 111269 | 3211 | Brazil/Cuba |
| 179 | 111369 | 0311 | Colombia/Cuba |
| 180 | 111869 | 0910 | Mexico/Cuba |
| 181 | 112069 | 2811 | Poland/Austria |
| 182 | 113169 | 3211 | Brazil/Cuba |
| 183 | 120269 | 0111 | USA/Cuba TWA |
| 184 | 121169 | 2911 | Korea/N. Korea |
| 185 | 121369 | 2101 | Ethiopia/Yemen |
| 186 | 121969 | 3401 | Chile/Cuba |
| 187 | 122369 | 3511 | Costa Rica/Cuba |
| 188 | 122669 | 0111 | USA/Cuba UAL |
|  | Dec. '69 | 2101 | Ethiopia/unknown |
| 189 | 010170 | 3211 | Brazil/Cuba |
| 190 | 010670 | 0101 | USA/Switzerland DL |
| 191 | 010770 | 3601 | Spain/Albania |
| 192 | 010870 | 0111 | USA/Lebanon TWA |
| 193 | 010970 | 3701 | Panama/Cuba |
| 194 | 012470 | 3811 | Netherlands Antilles/Cuba |
| 195 | 020670 | 3401 | Chile/Cuba |
| 196 | 021070 | 1901 | Israel/Libya |
| 197 | 021670 | 0111 | USA/Cuba EA |
| 198 | 031070 | 3901 | E. Germany/Unknown |
| 199 | 031170 | 0111 | USA/Cuba UN |
| 200 | 031170 | 0311 | Colombia/Cuba |
| 201 | 031270 | 3211 | Chile/Cuba |
| 202 | 031770 | 0101 | USA/Indefinite** EA |
| 203 | 032470 | 0711 | Argentina/Cuba |
| 204 | 032570 | 4110 | British Honduras/Cuba |
| 205 | 033070 | 4011 | Japan/N. Korea |
| 206 | 042270 | 0101 | USA/Indefinite** N. Central |
| 207 | 042270 | 0110 | USA/Cuba |
| 208 | 042570 | 3211 | Brazil/Cuba |
| 209 | 040170 | 4201 | Trinidad/Algeria (landed Havana) |
| 210 | 050570 | 1710 | Czechoslovakia/Austria |
| 211 | 051270 | 3811 | Curacao/Cuba |
| 212 | 051470 | 1401 | Australia/Unknown |
| 213 | 051470 | 3211 | Brazil/Cuba |
| 214 | 052170 | 0311 | Colombia/Cuba |
| 215 | 052470 | 0911 | Mexico/Cuba |
| 216 | 052570 | 0111 | USA/Cuba DL |
| 217 | 052570 | 0111 | USA/Cuba AA |
| 218 | 053070 | 4311 | Italy/Egypt |
| 219 | 053170 | 0311 | Colombia/Cuba |
| 220 | 060470 | 0101 | USA/Indefinite** TWA |
| 221 | 060570 | 2801 | Poland/Copenhagen |
| 222 | 060870 | 1711 | Czechoslovakia/W. Germany |

** There did not appear to be any particular location to which the aircraft was being diverted.

| 223 | 060970 | 2801 | Poland/Austria |
| 224 | NOTE: SEE ITEM FOLLOWING ITEM 188 | | |
| 225 | 062170 | 4401 | Iran/Iraq |
| 226 | 062270 | 0111 | USA/Egypt PAA |
| 227 | 062670 | 0410 | Venezuela/Colombia |
| 228 | 070170 | 0111 | USA/Cuba NAL |
| 229 | 070170 | 3201 | Brazil/Cuba |
| 230 | 070470 | 3201 | Brazil/Cuba |
| 231 | 071170 | 4501 | Saudi Arabia/Syria |
| 232 | 072270 | 4601 | S. Vietnam/Hong Kong |
| 233 | 072270 | 1811 | Greece/Egypt |
| 234 | 072570 | 0911 | Mexico/Cuba |
| 235 | 072870 | 0701 | Argentina/Cuba |